Stephen Duro
FINGER JOGGING B(

17 pieces in lighter styles for the young pianist

The Associated Board of
the Royal Schools of Music

FINGER JOGGING BOOGIE

STEPHEN DURO

A Raggy Tune

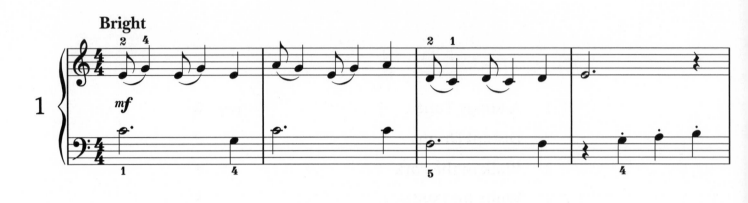

AB 2488

Distant Drums

Mysteriously

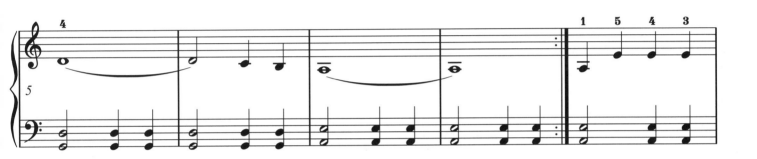

AB 2488

Walk in the Park

Strolling tempo

AB 2488

Waltz for Denise

Slow waltz time

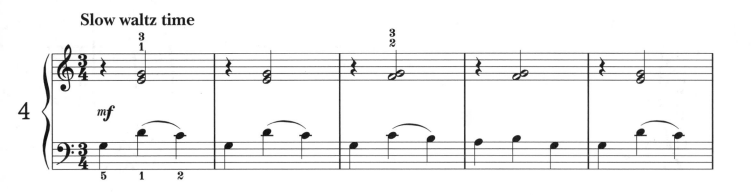

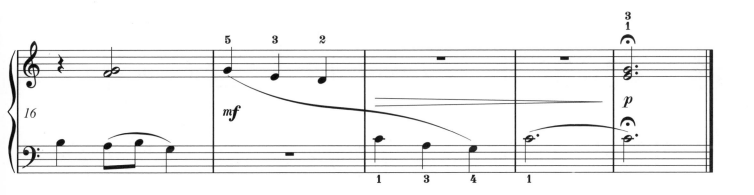

Finger Jogging Boogie

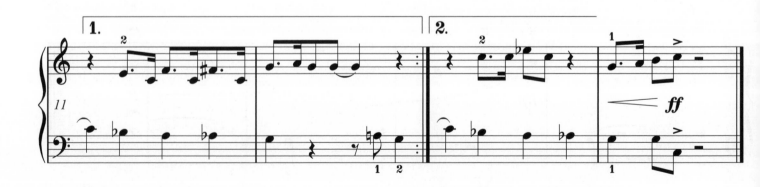

Rainy Day

Jaunty Blues

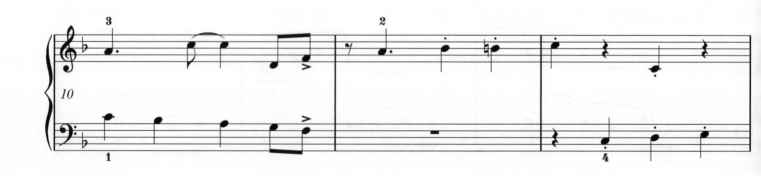

Swinging Along

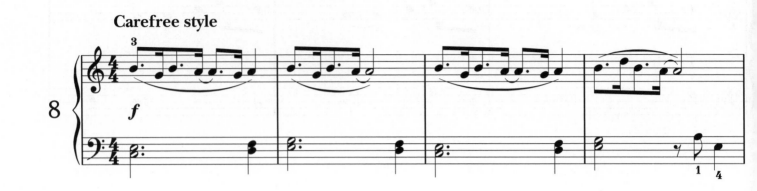

Calypso Joe

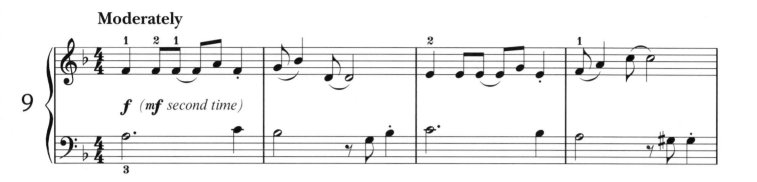

Up and Down the Stairs

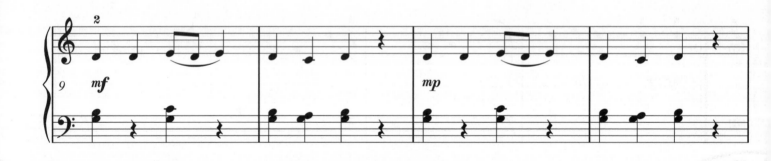

Now Listen to my Story

Happy-Go-Lucky Cha Cha

Song of the Pine Tree

Boston to Dover

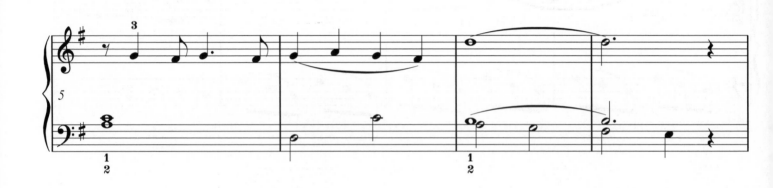

One and a Half Minute Waltz

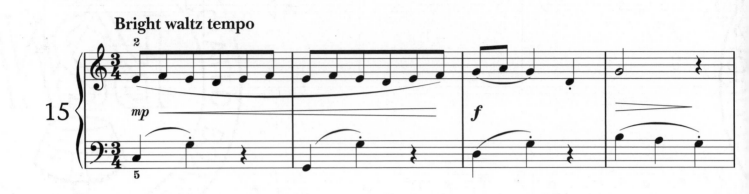

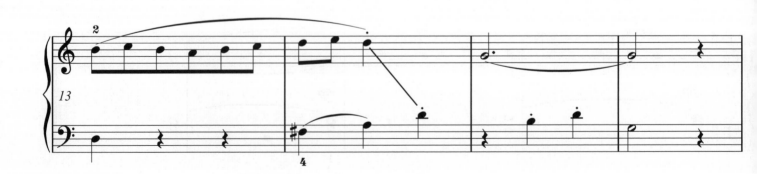

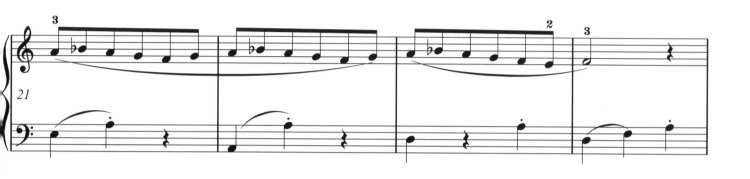

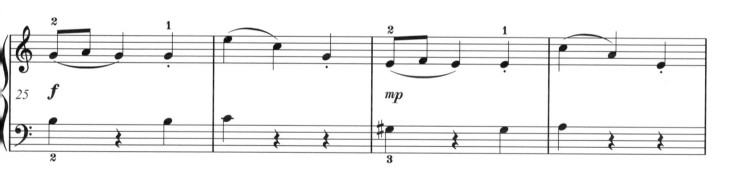

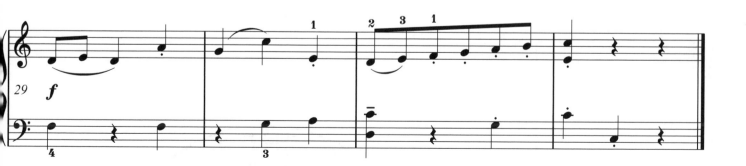

Peppermint Rock

Bygone Dreams

Printed by Caligraving Limited Thetford Norfolk England   AB 2488

KS3
Success

WORKBOOK

English

Kath Jordan

Contents

Reading fiction

Reading poetry

Reading non-fiction

Reading media texts

Writing

Shakespeare

Spelling, punctuation and grammar

Test practice

Homework diary

TOPIC	STUDY DATE	SCORE
Post-1914 fiction		/22
Pre-1914 fiction		/22
Comparing texts		/22
'Hide and Seek'		/22
'Nettles'		/22
Autobiography/recount		/22
Information and explanation		/22
Persuasion and argument		/22
Media texts		/22
Writing to describe		/25
Writing to imagine, explore, entertain		/35
Writing to argue and persuade		/35
Writing to advise		/35
Writing to inform and explain		/25
Writing to review, analyse, comment		/25
Romeo and Juliet: Act III Scene 2		/22
Romeo and Juliet: Act III Scene 5		/22
As You Like It: Act I Scene 1		/22
As You Like It: Act II Scene 3		/22
The Tempest: Act II Scene 2		/22
The Tempest: Act III Scene 2		/22
Spelling		/32
Punctuation and grammar		/32

How each topic will help you revise

The different topics covered in this workbook will help you to prepare for teacher assessed assignments, APP and the Optional Tests.

The reading topics

The reading topics cover pre- and post-1914 fiction, poetry and a range of non-fiction and media texts. If you are sitting the Year 9 Optional Test, you will be expected to read three text extracts and answer 15 questions covering a range of assessment focuses. The test is 1 hour and 15 minutes.

The writing topics

The writing topics cover a full range of purposes for writing. If you are sitting the Year 9 Optional Test, you will be expected to complete two writing tasks covering two different purposes. One task lasts 30 minutes and is worth 20 marks, the other lasts 45 minutes and is worth 30 marks.

The Shakespeare topics

If you are sitting the Year 9 Optional Test you will be expected to complete one task focusing on the set scenes from the Shakespeare play you have studied. The task you complete will be based on one of four areas of assessment: text in performance; character and motivation; language of the text; ideas, themes and issues. The test is 45 minutes.

The Spelling, Punctuation and Grammar topics

If you are sitting the Year 9 Optional Test, you will be awarded marks specifically for sentence structure, text organisation and spelling in the Writing Paper. Accurate SPG will make your answers clearer in all assessments.

Post-1914 fiction

Read the extract carefully and answer the questions that follow.

In this extract Kingshaw, the young boy, has gone for a walk to escape the bully he and his mother are staying with. In the isolated cornfields some way from the house, he has a terrifying experience when he is chased by an unexpected predator.

When he first saw the crow he took no notice. There had been several crows. This one glided into the corn on its enormous, ragged black wings. He began to be aware of it when it rose up suddenly, circled overhead, and then dived, to land not very far away from him. Kingshaw could see the feathers on its head, shining black in between the butter-coloured cornstalks. Then it rose, and circled, and came down again, this time not quite landing, but flapping about his head, beating its wings and making a sound like flat leather pieces being slapped together. It was the largest crow he had ever seen. As it came down for the third time, he looked up and noticed its beak, opening in a screech. The inside of its mouth was scarlet, it had small glinting eyes.

Kingshaw got up and flapped his arms. For a moment, the bird retreated a little way off, and higher up in the sky. He began to walk rather quickly back, through the path in the corn, looking ahead of him. Stupid to be scared of a rotten bird. What could a bird do? But he felt his own extreme isolation, high up in the cornfield.

For a moment, he could only hear the soft thudding of his own footsteps, and the silky sound of the corn, brushing against him. Then there was a rush of air, as the great crow came beating down, and wheeled about his head. The beak opened and the hoarse caw came out again and again, from inside the scarlet mouth.

Kingshaw began to run, not caring now, if he trampled the corn, wanting to get away, down into the next field. He thought that the corn might be some kind of crow's food store, in which he was seen as an invader. Perhaps this was only the first of a whole battalion of crows, that would rise up and swoop at him. Get on the grass then, he thought, get on to the grass, that'll be safe, it'll go away. He wondered if it had mistaken him for some hostile animal, lurking down in the corn.

His progress was very slow, through the cornfield, the thick stalks bunched together and got in his way, and he had to shove them back with his arms. But he reached the gate and climbed it, and dropped on to the grass of the field on the other side. Sweat was running down his forehead and into his eyes. He looked up. The crow kept on coming. He ran.

But it wasn't easy to run down this field, either, because of the tractor ruts. He began

to leap wildly from side to side of them, his legs stretched as far as they could go, and for a short time, it seemed that he did go faster. The crow dived again, and, as it rose, Kingshaw felt the tip of its black wing, beating against his face. He gave a sudden, dry sob. Then his left foot caught in one of the ruts and he keeled over, going down straight forwards.

He lay with his face in the coarse grass, panting and sobbing by turns, with the sound of his own blood pumping through his ears. He felt the sun on the back of his neck, and his ankle was wrenched. But he would be able to get up. He raised his head, and wiped two fingers across his face. A streak of blood came off, from where a thistle had scratched him. He got unsteadily to his feet, taking in deep, desperate breaths of the close air. He could not see the crow.

But when he began to walk forwards again, it rose up from the grass a little way off, and began to circle and swoop. Kingshaw broke into a run, sobbing and wiping the damp mess of tears and sweat off his face with one hand. There was a blister on his ankle, rubbed raw by the sandal strap. The crow was still quite high, soaring easily, to keep pace with him. Now, he had scrambled over the third gate, and he was in the field next to the one that belonged to Warings. He could see the back of the house, he began to run much faster.

This time, he fell and lay completely winded. Through the runnels of sweat and the sticky tufts of his own hair, he could see a figure looking down at him from one of the top windows of the house.

Then, there was a single screech, and the terrible beating of wings, and the crow swooped down and landed in the middle of his back.

Kingshaw thought that, in the end, it must have been his screaming that frightened it off, for he dared not move. He lay and closed his eyes and felt the claws of the bird, digging into his skin, through the thin shirt, and began to scream in a queer, gasping sort of way. After a moment or two, the bird rose. He had expected it to begin pecking at him with its beak, remembering terrible stories about vultures that went for living people's eyes. He could not believe in his own escape.

From *I'm the King of the Castle*
by Susan Hill

Post-1914 fiction: questions

A

Choose just one answer, a, b, c or d.

1 **Kingshaw is frightened because** (1 mark)

a) he is lost in a cornfield ☐

b) he is lost in a forest ☐

c) he is being chased by a vulture ☐

d) he is being chased by a crow ☐

2 '. . . a sound like flat leather pieces being slapped together' is (1 mark)

a) a metaphor ☐

b) a simile ☐

c) personification ☐

d) onomatopoeia ☐

3 **Kingshaw found it difficult to run in the cornfield because** (1 mark)

a) the cornstalks got in the way ☐

b) it was very muddy ☐

c) he had sprained his ankle ☐

d) the tractor ruts were too deep ☐

4 **The bird hurt Kingshaw by** (1 mark)

a) landing on his head ☐

b) pecking at his eyes ☐

c) digging its claws in his back ☐

d) knocking him to the ground ☐

5 **Kingshaw escaped because** (1 mark)

a) he ran away ☐

b) the bird flew away ☐

c) he chased the bird away ☐

d) his friend saved him ☐

Score / 5

B

Answer all parts of all questions.

1 **Look at the section 'Kingshaw got up and flapped his arms' to 'lurking down in the corn'.**

From this section, how do we know what Kingshaw is feeling?

Give two examples of what he thinks or does and explain how this shows what he is feeling. (4 marks)

Example:...

Explanation: ....

....

Example:...

Explanation: ....

....

2 **Look at the paragraph beginning 'His progress was very slow'.**

a) What do you notice about the sentences at the end of this paragraph? (1 mark)

....

b) What is the effect of this? (2 marks)

....

Score / 7

C Your answer should respond to each of the bullet points.

1 **How does the writer of this passage build increasing tension through this text?**

You should write about:

• the setting

• the structure of the text

• the way the character reacts to his situation. (10 marks)

....

....

....

....

....

....

....

....

....

....

....

....

....

....

....

....

....

....

....

....

....

....

....

....

....

Score   / 10

Total score   / 22

How well did you do?   ✗   0–6 **Try again**   7–10 **Getting there**   11–14 **Good work**   15–22 **Excellent!** ✓

For more help on this topic see **KS3 English Success Guide** pages **10–15**.

Pre-1914 fiction

Read the extract carefully and answer the questions that follow.

In this extract Mr Lockwood, the narrator, is visiting Wuthering Heights. Bad weather and heavy snowfall across the Yorkshire Moors prevent him from leaving for home. Heathcliff, the ill-tempered owner of Wuthering Heights, is reluctant to allow Lockwood to stay for the night but a servant takes pity on him and shows him upstairs. He finds a disused room with a large oak bed next to a window ledge and decides to sleep there. That night he is unable to sleep well as he is plagued by bad dreams and noises outside the window.

This text was written in the nineteenth century so you may find some of the language difficult and unfamiliar. A glossary is provided at the end of the extract to help you with some of the unfamiliar vocabulary.

This time, I remembered I was lying in the oak closet, and I heard distinctly the gusty wind, and the driving snow; I heard also, the fir-bough repeat its teasing sound, and ascribed it to the right cause: but it annoyed me so much, that I resolved to silence it, if possible; and, I thought, I rose and endeavoured to unhasp the casement. The hook was soldered into the staple: a circumstance observed by me when awake, but forgotten.

'I must stop it, nevertheless!' I muttered, knocking my knuckles through the glass, and stretching an arm out to seize the importunate branch: instead of which, my fingers closed on the fingers of a little, ice-cold hand!

The intense horror of nightmare came over me; I tried to draw back my arm, but the hand clung to it, and a most melancholy voice sobbed,

'Let me in – let me in!'

'Who are you?' I asked, struggling, meanwhile, to disengage myself.

'Catherine Linton,' it replied. 'I'm come home: I'd lost my way on the moor!'

As it spoke, I discerned, obscurely, a child's face looking through the window.

Terror made me cruel; and, finding it useless to attempt shaking the creature off, I pulled its wrist on to the broken pane, and rubbed it to and fro till blood ran down and soaked the bed-clothes: still it wailed, 'Let me in!' and maintained its tenacious grip, almost maddening me with fear.

'How can I?' I said at length. 'Let *me* go, if you want me to let you in!'

The fingers relaxed, I snatched mine through the hole, hurriedly piled the books up in a pyramid against it, and stopped my ears to exclude the lamentable prayer.

I seemed to keep them closed above a quarter of an hour, yet, the instant I listened again, there was the doleful cry moaning on!

'Begone!' I shouted, 'I'll never let you in, not if you beg for twenty years!'
'It's twenty years,' mourned the voice, 'twenty years, I've been a waif for twenty years!'

From *Wuthering Heights*
by Emily Brontë (1818–1848)

Glossary   Ascribed: put it down to
Unhasp: unhook
Casement: window
Importunate: persistent/annoying
Discerned, obscurely: saw but not clearly
Tenacious: stubborn/firm

'Begone!' I shouted, 'I'll never let you in, not if you beg for twenty years!'
'It's twenty years,' mourned the voice, 'twenty years, I've been a waif for twenty years!'

Pre-1914 fiction: questions

A

Choose just one answer, a, b, c or d.

1 **Which of the following words is *not* a synonym (alternative) for *lamentable*?** (1 mark)

a) laudable ☐

b) sorrowful ☐

c) sad ☐

d) woeful ☐

2 **The viewpoint in this text is** (1 mark)

a) 1st person ☐

b) 2nd person ☐

c) 3rd person ☐

d) omniscient ☐

3 **At first the narrator believes the noise that wakes him is** (1 mark)

a) a child ☐

b) a bad dream ☐

c) a tree branch tapping on the window ☐

d) a ghost ☐

4 **The words *he*, *she*, *it* are** (1 mark)

a) nouns ☐

b) verbs ☐

c) adverbs ☐

d) pronouns ☐

5 **The sentence type most often used in the dialogue (conversation) is** (1 mark)

a) interrogative ☐

b) exclamatory ☐

c) directive (imperative) ☐

d) declarative ☐

Score / 5

B

Answer all parts of all questions.

1 **Look again at the section beginning '"Who are you?" I asked'.**

a) Which pronoun does the author use to write about Catherine Linton and which pronoun would you expect the author to use? (2 marks)

Pronoun used: ....

Pronoun expected: ....

b) What effect does the author's choice of pronoun have? (2 marks)

....

....

2 **How would you describe the atmosphere of this text?**
List four words or phrases that help to create this atmosphere.

Atmosphere: ....

.... (1 mark)

Words and phrases: ....

.... (2 marks)

Score / 7

Your answers should respond to each of the bullet points.

1 **Does the narrator show any sympathy towards Catherine Linton?**

You should write about:

• the language he uses to describe her

• what he says to her

• the way he behaves.

(5 marks)

....

....

....

....

....

....

....

....

....

....

How does the author create a feeling of fear and horror in this passage?

You should write about:

• the way the setting is described

• the language used in the extract

• the way the narrator behaves.

(5 marks)

....

....

....

....

....

....

....

....

....

Score   / 10

Total score   / 22

How well did you do?   ✗   0–6 Try again   7–10 Getting there   11–14 Good work   15–22 Excellent! ✓

For more help on this topic see KS3 English Success Guide pages 10–15.

Comparing texts

Read the two extracts carefully and answer the questions that follow.

In this extract Mr Sugden, the PE teacher, punishes Billy for playing badly in a football match by making him take a cold shower. Mr Sugden uses his authority to bully and intimidate Billy, his pupil.

He undressed quickly, bending his pumps free of his heels and sliding them off without untying the laces. When he stood up the black soles of his socks stamped damp imprints on the dry floor, which developed into a haphazard set of footprints when he removed his socks and stepped around pulling his jeans down. His ankles and knees were ingrained with ancient dirt which seemed to belong to the pigmentation of his skin. His left leg sported a mud stripe, and both his knees were encrusted. The surfaces of these mobile crusts were hair-lined, and with every flexion of the knee these lines opened into frown-like furrows.

For an instant, as he hurried into the showers, with one leg angled in running, with his dirty legs and huge rib cage moulding the skin of his white body, with his hollow cheek in profile, and the sabre of shadow emanating from the eye-hole, just for a moment he resembled an old print of a child hurrying towards the final solution.

* * *

While he worked on his ankles and heels Sugden stationed three boys at one end of the showers and moved to the other end, where the controls fed into the pipes on the wall . . . The blunt arrow was pointing to HOT. Sugden swung it back over WARM to COLD. For a few seconds there was no visible change in the temperature, and the red slice held steady, still dominating the dial. Then it began to recede, slowly at first, then swiftly, its share of the face diminishing rapidly.

The cold water made Billy gasp. He held out his hands as though testing for rain, then ran for the end. The three guards barred the exit.

'Hey up, shift! Let me out, you rotten dogs!' They held him easily so he swished back to the other end, yelling all the way along. Sugden pushed him in the chest as he clung his way round the corner.

'Got a sweat on, Casper?'

'Let me out, Sir. Let me come.'

'I thought you'd like a cooler after your exertions in goal.'

'I'm frozen!'

'Really?'

'Gi' o'er, Sir! It's not right!'

'And was it right when you let the last goal in?'

'I couldn't help it!'

'Rubbish, lad.'

Billy tried another rush. Sugden repelled it, so he tried the other end again. Every time he tried to escape the three boys bounced him back, stinging him with their snapping towels as he retreated. He tried manoeuvring the nozzles, but whichever way he twisted them the water still found him out. Until finally he gave up, and stood amongst them, tolerating the freezing spray in silence.

From *A Kestrel for a Knave*
by Barry Hines

Glossary   Final solution: in World War II, Hitler's 'final solution' was to kill millions of Jews. Many of them were killed by gassing in mass showers.

In this extract George and Lennie meet Curley, the boss's son, for the first time. Curley uses his physical presence and aggression to intimidate Lennie.

His eyes passed over the new men and he stopped. He glanced coldly at George and then at Lennie. His arms gradually bent at the elbows and his hands closed into fists. He stiffened and went into a slight crouch. His glance was at once calculating and pugnacious. Lennie squirmed under the look and shifted his feet nervously. Curley stepped gingerly close to him. 'You the new guys the old man was waitin' for?'

'We just come,' said George.

'Let the big guy talk.'

Lennie twisted with embarrassment.

George said: 'S'pose he don't want to talk?'

Curley lashed his body around. 'By Christ, he's gotta talk when he's spoke to. What the hell are you gettin' into it for?'

'We travel together,' said George coldly.

'Oh, so it's that way.'

George was tense and motionless. 'Yeah, it's that way.'

Lennie was looking helplessly to George for instruction.

'An' you won't let the big guy talk, is that it?'

'He can talk if he wants to tell you anything.' He nodded slightly to Lennie.

'We jus' come in,' said Lennie softly.

Curley stared levelly at him. 'Well, nex' time you answer when you're spoke to.' He turned towards the door and walked out, and his elbows were still bent out a little.

George watched him out, and then turned back to the swamper. 'Say what the hell's he got on his shoulder? Lennie didn't do nothing to him.'

The old man looked cautiously at the door to make sure no one was listening. 'That's the boss's son,' he said quietly. 'Curley's pretty handy. He's done quite a bit in the ring. He's a lightweight, and he's handy.'

'Well let him be handy,' said George. 'He don't have to take after Lennie. Lennie didn't do nothing to him. What's he got against Lennie?'

The swamper considered: '– Well – tell you what. Curley's like a lot of little guys. He hates big guys. He's alla time picking scraps with big guys. Kind of like he's mad at 'em because he ain't a big guy. You seen little guys like that, ain't you? Always scrappy?'

'Sure,' said George. 'I seen plenty tough little guys. But this Curley better not make no mistakes about Lennie. Lennie ain't handy, but this Curley punk is gonna get hurt if he messes around with Lennie.'

From *Of Mice and Men*
by John Steinbeck

Comparing texts: questions

A

Choose just one answer, a, b, c or d.

1 **Mr Sugden was angry with Billy because** (1 mark)

a) he let a goal in ☐

b) he refused to have a shower ☐

c) he bullied another pupil ☐

d) he wouldn't join in the PE lesson ☐

2 **Another verb that means *tolerate* is** (1 mark)

a) enjoy ☐

b) endure ☐

c) refuse ☐

d) fight ☐

3 **Which punctuation mark is used most in the speech of Billy and Mr Sugden?** (1 mark)

a) comma ☐

b) question mark ☐

c) full stop ☐

d) exclamation mark ☐

4 **Which verb is *not* used to describe Lennie's movement?** (1 mark)

a) squirmed ☐

b) shifted ☐

c) shuffled ☐

d) twisted ☐

5 **In the second extract the reader's sympathy is with** (1 mark)

a) Curley ☐

b) Lennie ☐

c) George ☐

d) the swamper ☐

Score / 5

B

Answer all parts of all questions.

1 **Look closely at the way the dialogue is punctuated in the first extract.**
Give the two main punctuation marks used and explain what effect this has.

Punctuation: .... (1 mark)

Explanation: .... (1 mark)

2 **Look closely at the section beginning 'For an instant' (*A Kestrel for a Knave*).**
Explain how this comparison creates sympathy for Billy. (2 marks)

....

....

....

3 **Look closely at the section beginning 'His eyes passed over the new men' and ending 'What the hell are you gettin' into it for?' (*Of Mice and Men*).**

Give two words or phrases used to make Curley seem threatening and explain why they are effective.

Words and phrases: .... (1 mark)

Explanation: .... (2 marks)

Score / 7

C Your answer should respond to each of the bullet points.

1 **Compare the ways in which the two writers create sympathy for the victims of bullying and intimidation.**

You should write about:

• the way Billy and Lennie react to their situations

• the way the bullies are presented

• the way that other characters behave towards and talk about the main characters. **(10 marks)**

....

....

....

....

....

....

....

....

....

....

....

....

....

....

....

....

....

....

....

....

....

....

....

....

Score / 10

Total score / 22

How well did you do? ✗ 0–6 **Try again** 7–10 **Getting there** 11–14 **Good work** 15–22 **Excellent!** ✓

For more help on this topic see KS3 English Success Guide pages 10–15.

17

Hide and Seek

Read both poems carefully and answer the questions that follow.

Hide and Seek

Call out. Call loud: "I'm ready! Come and find me!"
The sacks in the toolshed smell like the seaside.
They'll never find me in this salty dark,
But be careful that your feet aren't sticking out.
Wiser not to risk another shout.
The floor is cold. They'll probably be searching
The bushes, near the swing. Whatever happens
You mustn't sneeze when they come prowling in.
And here they are, whispering at the door;
You've never heard them sound so hushed before.
Don't breathe. Don't move. Stay dumb. Hide in your blindness.
They're moving closer, someone stumbles, mutters;
Their words and laughter scuffle and they're gone.
But don't come out just yet; they'll try the lane,
And then the greenhouse and back here again.
They must be thinking that you're very clever,
Getting more puzzled as they search all over.
It seems a long time since they went away.
Your legs are stiff, the cold bites through your coat.
The dark damp smell of sand moves in your throat.
It's time to let them know that you're the winner
Push off the sacks. Uncurl and stretch. That's better!
Out of the shed and call to them "I've won!
Here I am! Come and own up I've caught you!"
The darkening garden watches. Nothing stirs.
The bushes hold their breath; the sun is gone.
Yes, here you are. But where are they who sought you?

Vernon Scannell

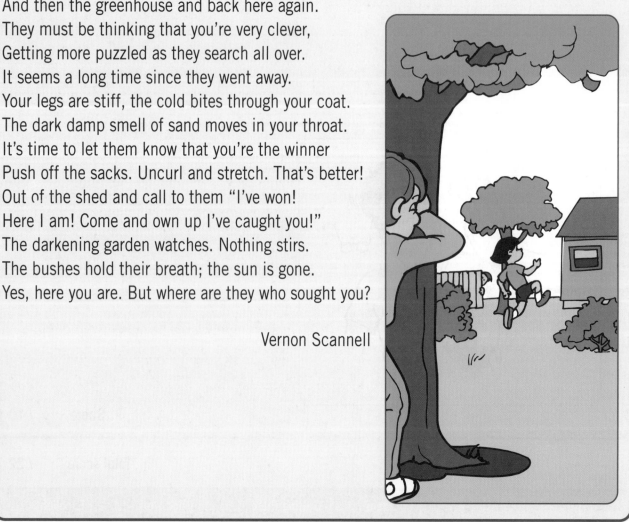

Nettles

My son aged three fell in the nettle bed.
'Bed' seemed a curious name for those green spears,
That regiment of spite behind the shed:
It was no place for rest. With sobs and tears
The boy came seeking comfort and I saw
White blisters beaded on his tender skin.
We soothed him till his pain was not so raw.
At last he offered us a watery grin,
And then I took my billhook, honed the blade
And went outside and slashed in fury with it
Till not a nettle in that fierce parade
Stood upright any more. Next task: I lit
A funeral pyre to burn the fallen dead,
But in two weeks the busy sun and rain
Had called up tall recruits behind the shed:
My son would often feel sharp wounds again.

Vernon Scannell

Glossary   Billhook: a traditional cutting tool
with wooden handle and metal
blade used for cutting down
shrubs etc.

Hide and Seek: questions

A

Choose just one answer, a, b, c or d.

1 The entire poem 'Hide and Seek' is written in   (1 mark)
- a) rhyming couplets ☐
- b) rhyming triplets ☐
- c) a regular rhyme scheme ☐
- d) an irregular rhyme scheme ☐

2 Where is the boy hiding?   (1 mark)
- a) the greenhouse ☐
- b) the back lane ☐
- c) the shed ☐
- d) the garage ☐

3 'the cold bites through your coat' is   (1 mark)
- a) juxtaposition ☐
- b) personification ☐
- c) an oxymoron ☐
- d) a simile ☐

4 Which of the following techniques is not used in the poem?   (1 mark)
- a) onomatopoeia ☐
- b) personification ☐
- c) rhyme ☐
- d) sensory imagery ☐

5 How many different voices can you hear in the poem?   (1 mark)
- a) one ☐
- b) two ☐
- c) three ☐
- d) four ☐

Score   / 5

B

Answer all parts of all questions.

1 Put the events of the poem in order by numbering the statements below.   (1 mark)

☐ The boy discovers he has been left all alone

☐ The boy hears muttering and laughter outside the shed

☐ The boy calls out to let his friends know he's ready

☐ The boy calls out to say he is the winner

2 The poet uses personification to create a slightly sinister effect. Give two examples of personification from the poem and explain how they create this effect.   (4 marks)

....

....

....

....

3 Explain the effect of the punctuation in the line 'Don't breathe. Don't move. Stay dumb'.   (2 marks)

....

....

Score   / 7

C

Your answers should respond to each of the bullet points.

1 The poem is written largely in the second person but also includes some lines in the first person. Explain the impact of the writer's viewpoint.

You should write about:

• the use of second person

• the impact of the words spoken directly by the child. (4 marks)

....

....

....

....

....

....

2 How does the poet use sensory images to make the reader feel involved in the poem?

You should write about:

• specific images from the poem

• how the poet might appeal to the reader's senses. (6 marks)

....

....

....

....

....

....

....

....

Score   / 10

Total score   / 22

How well did you do?   ✗   0–6 **Try again**   7–10 **Getting there**   11–14 **Good work**   15–22 **Excellent!**   ✓

For more help on this topic see KS3 English Success Guide pages 18–23.

Nettles: questions

A

Choose just one answer, a, b, c or d.

1 The poem 'Nettles' is about   (1 mark)

a) the poet being stung by nettles as an adult ☐

b) the poet being stung by nettles as a child ☐

c) the poet's son being stung by nettles ☐

d) the poet's daughter being stung by nettles ☐

2 'green spears' is   (1 mark)

a) alliteration ☐

b) personification ☐

c) a simile ☐

d) a metaphor ☐

3 Which statement best describes the rhyme scheme of the poem?   (1 mark)

a) rhyming couplets ☐

b) the poem has an 'abab' scheme ☐

c) the poem has an 'abcb' scheme ☐

d) there is no rhyme scheme ☐

4 What does the poet do with the nettles?   (1 mark)

a) cut them down and put them in the bin ☐

b) put weed killer on them ☐

c) cut them down and burn them ☐

d) fence them off ☐

5 Which of the following phrases is not used to describe the nettles?   (1 mark)

a) 'fierce parade' ☐

b) 'fallen dead' ☐

c) 'regiment of spite' ☐

d) 'new recruits' ☐

Score   / 5

B

Answer all parts of all questions.

1 Write down two metaphors used in the poem and explain why each is effective.   (4 marks)

Metaphor: ....

Explanation: ....

....

....

Metaphor: ....

Explanation: ....

....

....

2 What do you think the poet means when he says 'My son would often feel sharp wounds again'?   (2 marks)

....

....

3 Which word is used to personify the weather towards the end of the poem?   (1 mark)

....

Score   / 7

C

Your answers should respond to each of the bullet points.

1 **How does Scannell use this poem to explore the strong feelings parents have for their children?**

You should write about:

- The way he describes his son the child
- The way he describes the nettles
- The poet's feelings

(10 marks)

....
....
....
....
....
....
....
....
....
....
....
....
....
....
....
....
....
....
....
....
....
....
....

Score   / 10

Total score   / 22

How well did you do?   ✗   0–6 Try again   7–10 Getting there   11–14 Good work   15–22 Excellent!   ✓

For more help on this topic see KS3 English Success Guide pages 18–23.

Autobiography/recount

Read the extract carefully and answer the questions that follow.

This extract is from Nelson Mandela's autobiography *Long Walk to Freedom*. He writes about his rural African upbringing, his struggle against apartheid, his imprisonment and finally his election as President of South Africa. This extract is from the section entitled 'Robben Island: the dark years', in which he describes his prison life.

In the midst of breakfast, the guards would yell, 'Val in! Val in!' (Fall in! Fall in!), and we would stand outside our cells for inspection. Each prisoner was required to have the three buttons of his khaki jacket properly buttoned. We were required to doff our hats as the warder walked by. If our buttons were undone, our hats unremoved, or our cells untidy, we were charged with a violation of the prison code and punished with either solitary confinement or the loss of meals.

After inspection we would work in the courtyard hammering stones until noon. There were no breaks; if we slowed down the warders would yell at us to speed up. At noon, the bell would clang for lunch and another metal drum of food would be wheeled into the courtyard. For Africans, lunch consisted of boiled mealies, that is, coarse kernels of corn. The Indians and Coloured prisoners received samp, or mealie rice, which consisted of ground mealies in a soup-like mixture. The samp was sometimes served with vegetables, whereas our mealies were served straight.

For lunch we often received phuzamandla, which means 'drink of strength', a powder made from mealies and a bit of yeast. It is meant to be stirred into water or milk, and when it is thick it can be tasty, but the prison authorities gave us so little of the powder that it barely coloured the water. I would usually save my powder for several days until I had enough to make a proper drink, but if the authorities discovered you were hoarding food, the powder was confiscated and you were punished.

After lunch we worked until 4, when the guards blew shrill whistles and we once again lined up to be counted and inspected. We were then permitted half an hour to clean up. The bathroom at the end of our corridor had two seawater showers, a saltwater tap and three large galvanized metal buckets, which were used as bathtubs. There was no hot water. We would stand or squat in these buckets, soaping ourselves with the brackish water, rinsing off the dust from the day. To wash yourself with cold water when it is cold outside is not pleasant, but we made the best of it. We would sometimes sing while

24

washing, which made the water seem less icy. In those early days, this was one of the only times when we could converse.

Precisely at 4.30 there would be a loud knock on the wooden door at the end of the corridor, which meant that supper had been delivered. Common-law prisoners used to dish out the food to us and we would return to our cells to eat it. We again received mealie pap porridge, sometimes with the odd carrot or piece of cabbage or beetroot thrown in – but one usually had to search for it. If we did get a vegetable, we would usually have the same one for weeks on end, until the cabbage or carrots were old and mouldy and we thoroughly sick of them. Every other day we received a small piece of meat with our porridge. The meat was mostly gristle.

For supper, Coloured and Indian prisoners received a quarter loaf of bread (known as katkopf that is, a cat's head, after the shape of the bread) and a slab of margarine. Africans, it was presumed, did not care for bread as it was a 'European' type of food.

Typically, we received even less than the scanty amounts stipulated in the regulations. This was because the kitchen was rife with smuggling. The cooks – all of whom were common-law prisoners – kept the best food for themselves or their friends. Often they would lay aside the tastiest morsel for the warders in exchange for favours or preferential treatment.

At 8 p.m. the night warder would lock himself in the corridor with us, passing the key through a small hole in the door to another warder outside. The warder would then walk up and down the corridor, ordering us to go to sleep. No cry of 'lights out' was ever given on Robben Island because the single mesh-covered bulb in our cell burned day and night. Later, those studying for higher degrees were permitted to read until 10 or 11 p.m.

From *Long Walk to Freedom*
by Nelson Mandela

Autobiography/recount: questions

A

Choose just one answer, a, b, c or d.

1 *Katkopf* means (1 mark)

a) drink of strength ☐

b) fall in ☐

c) lights out ☐

d) cat's head ☐

2 **Prisoners had to go to sleep at** (1 mark)

a) 7 p.m. ☐

b) 8 p.m. ☐

c) 10 p.m. ☐

d) 11 p.m. ☐

3 **Which of the following is *not* normally a feature of a recount text?** (1 mark)

a) written in the present tense ☐

b) temporal (time) connectives ☐

c) events told in order ☐

d) focuses on specified individuals or groups ☐

4 **When was inspection?** (1 mark)

a) before breakfast ☐

b) after breakfast ☐

c) during breakfast ☐

d) before lights out ☐

5 **Africans didn't receive bread because** (1 mark)

a) they didn't like it ☐

b) the common-law prisoners stole it ☐

c) the prison authorities thought they didn't like 'European' food ☐

d) it was kept back as punishment ☐

Score / 5

B

Answer all parts of all questions.

1 **Which part of the prison routine is described in most detail? Explain what this detail emphasises. Find and copy a quotation to support your explanation.** (3 marks)

Part of routine: ....

Explanation: ....

.. ..

Quotation: ....

2 **This is a recount text. Find and copy an example of each of the following features of a recount.** (2 marks)

Temporal connective: ....

Focuses on individuals or identified groups: ....

....

3 **This extract uses language from another country. Find an example and explain how the meaning has been made clear to the reader.** (2 marks)

Example:..

Explanation: ....

....

Score / 7

C

Your answer should respond to each of the bullet points.

1 **Explain how the writer highlights the harshness of the routine and the prejudice he encountered whilst in prison.**

You should write about:

• the way he describes the daily routine

• what he does to cope with the routine

• his relationships with others

• punishments. (10 marks)

....

....

....

....

....

....

....

....

....

....

....

....

....

....

....

....

....

....

....

....

....

....

....

....

....

Score   / 10

Total score   / 22

How well did you do? ✗ 0–6 **Try again**   7–10 **Getting there**   11–14 **Good work**   15–22 **Excellent!** ✓

For more help on this topic see KS3 English Success Guide pages 26–33.

Key Facts about the United Kingdom

If you're looking for key facts about the UK and its overseas territories, there are good sources of information available online and elsewhere.

'UK' or 'Britain'?

The full title of this country is 'the United Kingdom of Great Britain and Northern Ireland':

• Great Britain is made up of England, Scotland and Wales

• the United Kingdom (UK) is made up of England, Scotland, Wales and Northern Ireland

• 'Britain' is used informally, usually meaning the United Kingdom.

The Channel Islands and the Isle of Man are not part of the UK. The geographical term 'British Isles' covers the UK, all of Ireland, the Channel Islands and the Isle of Man.

Population

In mid-2003 the UK was home to 59.6 million people. The average age was 38.4 years, an increase on 1971 when it was 34.1 years. There are more people in the UK aged over 60 (12.4 million), than there are children under 16 (11.7 million).

The UK has a growing population. It grew by 232,100 people in the year to mid-2003, and the growth was 0.4 per

cent in each of the years since mid-2001. The UK population has increased by 6.5 per cent in the last 30 years or so, from 55.9 million in mid-1971. It is one of the largest populations in the European Union (EU), accounting for 13 per cent of the total.

Every ten years, a population census takes place. Statistics for the last census (2001) are available online. Full details, including individual census returns, are available for the censuses held in 1901 and earlier.

National ceremonies and symbols

The union flag, the national anthem, currency, stamps and other national events help identify and symbolise what it is to be British and to live in the United Kingdom.

Flags

The Union Flag, or 'Union Jack', is the national flag of the United Kingdom and is so called because it embodies the emblems of the three countries united under one Sovereign - the kingdoms of England and Wales, of Scotland and of Ireland (although since 1921 only Northern Ireland, rather than the whole of Ireland, has been part of the United Kingdom).

The term 'Union Jack' possibly dates from Queen Anne's time (reigned 1702-14), but its origin is uncertain. It may come from the 'jack-et' of the English or Scottish soldiers; or from the name of James I (who originated the first union in 1603), in either its Latin or French form, 'Jacobus' or 'Jacques'; or, as 'jack' once meant small, the name may be derived from a royal proclamation issued by Charles II that the Union Flag should be flown only by ships of the Royal Navy as a jack, a small flag at the bowsprit.

The Department for Culture, Media and Sport provides information on how and when the Union Flag can be flown as well as information on which way up to fly it.

The Royal Standard represents the Sovereign and the United Kingdom. The Royal Standard is flown when The Queen is in residence in one of the Royal Palaces, on The Queen's car on official journeys and on aircraft. It may also be flown on any building, official or private (but not ecclesiastical buildings), during a visit by The Queen.

National anthem

'God Save The King' was a patriotic song first publicly performed in London in 1745, which came to be referred to as the National Anthem from the beginning of the nineteenth century. The words and tune are anonymous, and may date back to the seventeenth century. There is no authorised version of the National Anthem as the words are a matter of tradition.

Ceremonies

The armed forces are often involved in many of the great ceremonies of state. The Army website gives details of events such as trooping the colours, the state opening of Parliament, Remembrance Sunday and state visits.

Currency, coins and banknotes

The Bank of England has issued banknotes since it was founded in 1694. Its website provides information on the history and design of banknotes.

The Royal Mint can be traced back more than a thousand years and is still a department of government. Its main responsibility is the provision of the United Kingdom's coinage. The Mint's website sells coins and related collectables.

Stamps

The Royal Mail publishes stamps for the UK.

Symbols of the royal origins of the UK's postal system remain: a miniature silhouette of the Monarch's head is depicted on all stamps.

Great Seal

The Great Seal of the Realm is the chief seal of the Crown, used to show the monarch's approval of important state documents. In today's constitutional monarchy, the Sovereign acts on the advice of the Government of the day, but the seal remains an important symbol of the Sovereign's role as Head of State.

Royal Coat of Arms

The function of the Royal Coat of Arms is to identify the person who is Head of State. In the UK, the royal arms are borne only by the Sovereign. They are used in many ways in connection with the administration and government of the country, for instance on coins, in churches and on public buildings.

The coat of arms is familiar to most people as it appears on the products and goods of Royal Warrant holders.

The Crown Jewels

The crowns and treasures associated with the British Monarchy are powerful symbols of monarchy. For over 600 years kings and queens of England have stored crowns, robes and other valuable items of ceremonial regalia at the Tower of London. Since the 17th century, at least, this collection has been known as the 'Crown Jewels'.

Text taken from www.direct.gov.uk

© Crown copyright; layout by Letts Educational.

Information and explanation: questions

A

Choose just one answer, a, b, c or d.

1 Which is the correct term to describe England, Scotland, Wales, all of Ireland, the Channel Islands and the Isle of Man? *(1 mark)*

a) The British Empire ☐

b) Great Britain ☐

c) the United Kingdom ☐

d) the British Isles ☐

2 When was the first union of the United Kingdom formed? *(1 mark)*

a) 1921 ☐

b) 1603 ☐

c) 1702 ☐

d) 1714 ☐

3 Which of the following should not fly the Royal Standard? *(1 mark)*

a) a church ☐

b) royal palace ☐

c) official car ☐

d) aircraft ☐

4 Which organisation provides the UK's coins? *(1 mark)*

a) Bank of England ☐

b) Royal Mail ☐

c) Royal Mint ☐

d) Tower of London ☐

5 Which of the following features is not used in this information text? *(1 mark)*

a) bullet points ☐

b) sub headings ☐

c) short paragraphs ☐

d) columns ☐

Score   / 5

B

Answer all parts of all questions.

1 What technique has been used in the first sub-heading? Give one reason why it may have been used. *(2 marks)*

Technique: ....

Reason: ....

2 Comment on the use of punctuation in this text. *(3 marks)*

....

....

....

3 This article uses logical and temporal (time) connectives. Find and copy an example of each. *(2 marks)*

Logical: ....

Temporal: ....

Score   / 7

C

Your answer should respond to each of the bullet points.

1 **How do the language, structure and layout of this text make it successful as an information text?**

You should write about:

- The intended purpose and audience of the text
- Use of language
- Use of punctuation
- Organisation of the text
- Layout / presentation features

(10 marks)

....

....

....

....

....

....

....

....

....

....

....

....

....

....

....

....

....

....

....

....

....

....

Score   / 10

Total score   / 22

How well did you do?   ✗ 0–6 **Try again**   7–10 **Getting there**   11–14 **Good work**   15–22 **Excellent!** ✓

For more help on this topic see KS3 English Success Guide pages 26–33.

Persuasion and argument

Read the two extracts carefully and answer the questions that follow.

The extract printed below is the final part of a speech delivered by Tony Blair (British Prime Minister) after the start of the US and British military strikes on targets in Afghanistan on Sunday, 7th October 2001.

The world understands that whilst of course there are dangers in acting as we are, the dangers of inaction are far, far greater - the threat of further such outrages, the threats to our economies, the threat to the stability of the world.

On the humanitarian front, we are assembling a coalition of support for refugees in and outside Afghanistan, which is as vital as the military coalition. Even before September 11, four million Afghans were on the move. There are two million refugees in Pakistan and one and a half million in Iran. We have to ask for humanitarian reasons to alleviate the appalling suffering of the Afghan people and to deliver stability so that people from that region stay in that region. We have already contributed £36 million to the humanitarian effort and stand ready to do more. So we are taking action therefore on three fronts - military, diplomatic and humanitarian.

I also want to say very directly to the British people why this matters so much to Britain. First, let us not forget that the attacks of 11 September represented the worst terrorist outrage against British citizens in our history. The murder of British citizens, whether it happened overseas or not, is an attack upon Britain. But even if no British citizen had died, we would be right to act.

This atrocity was an attack on us all, on people of all faiths and people of none. We know the al-Qaeda network threatens Europe, including Britain, and indeed any nation throughout the world that does not share their fanatical views. So we have a direct interest in acting in our self-defence to protect British lives. It was an attack on lives and livelihoods.

The airlines, tourism and other industries have been affected, and economic confidence has suffered with all that means to British jobs and business. Our prosperity and standard of living require us to deal with the terrorist threat. We act also because the al-Qaeda network and the Taleban regime are funded in large parts on the drugs trade - 90% of all heroin sold in Britain originates from Afghanistan. Stopping that trade is again directly in our interests.

I wish to say finally, as I have said many times before, that this is not a war with Islam. It angers me, as it angers the vast majority of Muslims, to hear Bin Laden and his associates described as Islamic terrorists. They are terrorists pure and simple. Islam is a peaceful and tolerant religion, and the acts of these people are contrary to the teachings of the Koran.

These are difficult and testing times for us all. People are bound to be concerned about what the terrorists may seek to do in response.

I should say there is at present no specific credible threat to the United Kingdom that we know of and that we have in place tried and tested contingency plans which are the best possible response to any further attempts at terror. This is a moment of utmost gravity for the world. None of the leaders involved in this action want war. None of our nations want it. We are peaceful people.

But we know that sometimes to safeguard peace, we have to fight. Britain has learnt that lesson many times in our history. We only do it if the cause is just. This cause is just.

The writer of the following passage argues that watching television can be bad for your health.

Too much television can damage your child's health

Television may be part of everyday life for most children but is it safe? In our hectic lives we are so busy managing our private and professional concerns and relationships, we allow our children to spend a huge percentage of their unsupervised time watching television. So busy, in fact, that most of us don't stop to consider the hidden dangers of unlimited viewing.

The health risks which attend excessive television viewing are extensive and, to my mind, should not be underestimated. It contributes to the growing problems of adolescent obesity; it prevents regular exercise which could cause heart problems in later life; it causes psychological problems if children are exposed to inappropriate materials and it can damage eyesight.

However, the most worrying problem is the detrimental effect that too much television can have on the early stages of a child's development. Playing games, listening to stories and interacting with other children are all essential to a child's emotional, physical and communicational development. When television takes the place of these activities, we allow untold damage to be done.

Of course, many would be quick to defend the educational value of television and there is no doubt that properly managed television viewing can be beneficial. In my opinion, however, the dangers far outweigh the benefits. Until parents make time to exercise proper control over their children's viewing habits, children's health will continue to suffer.

Persuasion and argument: questions

A

Choose just one answer, a, b, c or d.

1 In the first paragraph of the extract from Tony Blair's speech, which word is used as the focus for a list of three? (1 mark)

a) outrage ☐

b) danger ☐

c) threat ☐

d) Britain ☐

2 Which of the following personal pronouns are used most in Tony Blair's speech? (1 mark)

a) he and she ☐

b) I and we ☐

c) you and it ☐

d) us and them ☐

3 The intended audience of 'Too much television' is (1 mark)

a) health professionals ☐

b) teachers ☐

c) children ☐

d) adults – particularly parents ☐

4 The sentence type used most in 'Too much television' is (1 mark)

a) simple ☐

b) complex ☐

c) compound ☐

d) interrogative ☐

5 The title 'Too much television can damage your child's health' is (1 mark)

a) a fact ☐

b) an opinion ☐

c) an opinion presented as fact ☐

d) a fact presented as opinion ☐

Score / 5

B

Answer all parts of all questions.

These questions all relate to 'Too much television can damage your child's health'.

1 Find and copy two connective words or phrases used in the passage. (1 mark)

a) ....

b) ....

2 What type of question is used in the first sentence? Explain the effect of opening the text in this way. (2 marks)

Question type: ....

Explanation: ....

3 Give two examples of problems caused by too much television viewing and explain why these problems occur. (4 marks)

Example: ....

Explanation: ....

Example: ....

Explanation: ....

Score / 7

C

Your second answer should respond to each of the bullet points.

These questions all relate to the extract from Tony Blair's speech

1 In the section beginning "I also want to say..." and ending "It was an attack on lives and livelihoods", how is the technique of repetition used and what is its intended effect on the listener? **(4 marks)**

....

....

....

....

....

....

2 Explain how some of the structures at text (paragraphing) and sentence level help to organise and develop the speaker's argument.

You should write about:

• The topic and order of the paragraphs

• Sentence length

• Specific examples of the way punctuation is used **(6 marks)**

....

....

....

....

....

....

....

....

....

....

....

....

....

....

Score   / 10

Total score   / 22

How well did you do?   ✗   0–6 Try again   7–10 Getting there   11–14 Good work   15–22 Excellent!   ✓

For more help on this topic see KS3 English Success Guide pages 26–33.

35

Media texts

Five-a-Day – The Easy Way!

This leaflet was produced to encourage healthy eating. It gives information about the benefits of healthy eating and recommendations about daily intake of fruit and vegetables.

It's never too early to introduce healthy habits

Healthy Eating can be Fun!

Of course you want what's best for your child but sometimes getting the balance right can be hard. All parents dread turning meal times into a battleground and it can be tempting to swap healthy fruit for a bowl of tempting ice cream. But healthy choices can also be fun. Follow this simple advice to avoid problems and keep mealtimes happy.

Fast Food Fun!

Fast food doesn't need to mean junk food. Fruit and vegetables make the ideal snacks: after school; after sports; on the move or for a TV treat:

- Bananas are the ultimate fast food, no preparation needed, just unzip and enjoy
- Dried apricots and raisins make a great alternative to sweets or chocolate
- Ready chopped sticks of carrot, cucumber and red or yellow pepper are delicious to crunch on with a favourite dip.
- Keep a bowl of ready washed and chopped fruit on an easy to reach shelf in the fridge and encourage your children to help themselves if they feel a bit peckish.

I hate sprouts!

Some vegetables do a have a strong taste which children may dislike. You could try disguising some of these stronger flavours by mixing with cheese sauce or tomato sauce. Many vegetables have naturally sweet flavours which will appeal to young children. Delicious puddings are easy to create with some added fruity goodness.

- Make your own tomato sauce. Onions, carrots, celery and peppers could be whizzed up with tinned tomatoes to make a delicious and versatile sauce. Try it as a pizza base, with pasta shapes or in your own Bolognese sauce.

- Broccoli or cauliflower cheese is a meal in itself or a tasty side dish.

- Add carrot or sweet potato to ordinary mashed potato
- Mix pureed fruit with Greek yoghurt or fromage frais
- Use fresh or tinned fruit in jellies

What counts in our Five-a-Day?

- Fresh fruit and vegetables
- Frozen vegetables
- Dried fruit
- Fresh fruit juice
- Tinned fruit and vegetables

Why is the Five-a-Day rule important?

Fruit and vegetables are full of vitamins, minerals and fibre – all essential for good health, especially when it comes to fighting off germs picked up at nursery or in the school playground. Experts are all in agreement that eating the recommended five portions of fruit or vegetables can lower the risk of serious health problems in later life including heart disease, cancer, stroke and type 2 diabetes. So if you want to give your child the best start in life, get started and go for five now!

Get stuck in!

Encourage your child to help you in the kitchen. They will be keen to eat it if they've helped to make it!

- Try making pizza together with that yummy tomato sauce
- Cheesy courgette muffins are hard to beat but simple to bake
- What about having your own take away night and making a quick and easy stir fry with lots of brightly coloured vegetables

Or what about growing your own fruit and vegetables? Even the smallest garden, yard or window box has room for a tomato plant or a pot of baby carrots.

If you would like more information about growing your own fruit and vegetables or quick and easy recipes for healthy meals and snacks, please complete the order form overleaf.

Media texts: questions

A

Choose just one answer, a, b, c or d.

1 **The purpose of this text is to** (1 mark)

a) entertain ☐

b) describe ☐

c) advise and persuade ☐

d) describe and persuade ☐

2 **The text is written in Standard English because it is aimed at** (1 mark)

a) doctors and health specialists ☐

b) children ☐

c) ordinary parents ☐

d) people living in the South of England ☐

3 **This leaflet contains** (1 mark)

a) facts only ☐

b) a mixture of fact and opinion ☐

c) opinions only ☐

d) instructions only ☐

4 **According to the leaflet fruit and vegetables contain lots of** (1 mark)

a) fat ☐

b) starch ☐

c) protein ☐

d) vitamins ☐

5 **Which of the following is not mentioned in 'What counts as 5-a-day'?** (1 mark)

a) fruit sweets ☐

b) tinned fruit ☐

c) frozen vegetables ☐

d) dried fruit ☐

Score / 5

B

Answer all parts of all questions.

1 **Which verb form is used in the 'I hate sprouts' section of the leaflet? Explain why this form is used.** (2 marks)

Verb form: ....

Explanation: ....

2 **Identify two layout/presentation features in the leaflet and explain why they have been used.** (2 marks)

Layout: ....

Explanation: ....

Layout: ....

Explanation: ....

3 **Discuss how the issue of 'Fast food' is tackled in this leaflet.** (3 marks)

....

....

....

....

Score / 7

C

1 **How does the leaflet aim to persuade parents to make more effort to get their children to eat more fruit and vegetables?**

You should write about:

• The language used

• The layout of the leaflet

• Whether you think the leaflet will be successful   (10 marks)

....

....

....

....

....

....

....

....

....

....

....

....

....

....

....

....

....

....

....

....

....

....

Score   **/ 10**

Total score   / 22

How well did you do?   ✗ 0–6 **Try again**   7–10 **Getting there**   11–14 **Good work**   15–22 **Excellent!** ✓

For more help on this topic see KS3 English Success Guide pages 36–43.

39

Writing to describe

A

Choose just one answer, a, b, c or d/true or false.

1 Descriptive writing   (1 mark)

a) is always factual ☐

b) is always fiction ☐

c) is always a balance of fact and fiction ☐

d) can be a mixture of fact and fiction ☐

2 An adverb   (1 mark)

a) describes a noun ☐

b) usually ends in *ed* ☐

c) describes a verb ☐

d) is a doing word ☐

3 When you are describing a person you should concentrate on what *he/she* looks like.   (1 mark)

true/false

4 Imagery such as simile and metaphor can be used in description.   (1 mark)

true/false

5 Sensory description is writing that   (1 mark)

a) describes your senses ☐

b) describes what you can see ☐

c) describes what you can hear ☐

d) describes what you can see, hear, touch, taste or smell ☐

Score   / 5

B

Use the space below to complete a spider diagram plan for the writing task in Section C.

Although this section doesn't carry a score, it will help you to score higher marks in Section C.

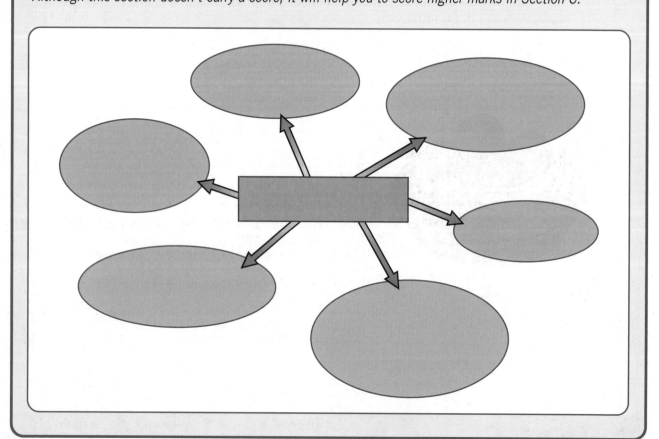

40

C

Your answer should respond to each of the bullet points. You should spend about 20 minutes writing. Continue your writing on a separate sheet if necessary.

1 **Write a brief description of your ideal holiday location. Write three paragraphs only.**

You could describe:

- the setting
- the atmosphere
- the people.

Remember to use descriptive vocabulary and imagery; try to appeal to the senses. (20 marks)

....

....

....

....

....

....

....

....

....

....

....

....

....

....

....

....

....

....

....

....

....

....

....

Score   / 20

Total score   / 25

Writing to imagine, explore, entertain

A

Choose just one answer, a, b, c or d/true or false.

1 **The structure of narrative writing is usually** (1 mark)

a) introduction, development, resolution, climax ☐

b) resolution, climax, introduction, development ☐

c) introduction, development, climax, resolution ☐

d) introduction, climax, development, resolution ☐

2 **The most important element(s) of narrative fiction is/are** (1 mark)

a) plot, description and dialogue ☐

b) plot ☐

c) dialogue ☐

d) plot and dialogue ☐

3 **An adjective** (1 mark)

a) usually ends in *ly* ☐

b) describes a noun ☐

c) describes a verb ☐

d) usually ends in *ed* ☐

4 **You should reveal everything about a character directly.** (1 mark)

true/false

5 **Dialogue should always be followed by a phrase such as 'Jamie said' to indicate who has spoken.** (1 mark)

true/false

Score / 5

B

Use the space below to complete a plan for the writing task in Section C.

Although this section doesn't carry a score, it will help you to score higher marks in Section C.

Main character factfile

....

....

....

....

....

....

....

....

....

....

....

....

Introduction

....

....

Development

....

....

Climax

....

....

Resolution

....

....

C

The bullet points are suggestions to help you complete the task. You should spend about 40 minutes writing. You should continue your writing on a separate sheet. Try not to write more than two sides of A4 paper.

Some of the 'Reading fiction' extracts in this book are about frightening experiences.

1 Imagine that you are trapped somewhere. Write the story of your escape.

You could:

• describe the place where you are trapped

• describe your feelings

• build up a tense or frightening atmosphere

• write about somebody else being trapped, if you prefer to write in the third person.

Remember to include a balance of plot development, description and dialogue. (30 marks)

Score / 30

Total score / 35

How well did you do?   ✗ 0–10 **Try again**   11–20 **Getting there**   21–25 **Good work**   26–35 **Excellent!** ✓

For more help on this topic see KS3 English Success Guide pages 46–51.

Writing to argue and persuade

A

Choose just one answer, a, b, c or d/true or false.

1 Opinions would not be used in persuasive writing. (1 mark)

true/false

2 A counter-argument is (1 mark)

a) a point that supports the main argument ☐

b) a point that opposes the main argument ☐

c) an argument that offends somebody ☐

d) an irrelevant point ☐

3 Which of the following could be used as a rhetorical question? (1 mark)

a) What is your name? ☐

b) What do you mean? ☐

c) If you feel the same way why don't you join us? ☐

d) What is your favourite colour? ☐

4 If you begin a formal letter *Dear Sir* you should end with (1 mark)

a) *Yours sincerely* ☐

b) *Yours faithfully* ☐

c) *Best wishes* ☐

d) *yours sincerely* ☐

5 When hand writing a letter your own address should be written (1 mark)

a) at the top right ☐

b) at the bottom right ☐

c) at the top left ☐

d) under the recipient's address ☐

Score / 5

B

Use the space below to complete a plan for the writing task in Section C.

Although this section doesn't carry a score, it will help you to score higher marks in Section C.

Use this space to record and organise the main points of your argument.

Points in favour of my argument

....

....

....

....

Use this space to note down emotive words/phrases, rhetorical questions, etc.

Word/phrase bank

....

....

....

....

The bullet points are suggestions to help you complete the task. You should spend about 40 minutes writing. You should continue your writing on a separate sheet. Try not to write more than two sides of A4 paper.

1 Write a letter to your local MP to persuade him/her to support your argument that more major sporting events should take place in the UK.

You could write about:

• the benefits for British sportsmen and sportswomen

• the benefits for local communities

• the international profile of the UK

• possible objections and how you would counter them.

Remember to write a formal letter. Try to be as persuasive as you can.

(30 marks)

....

....

....

....

....

....

....

....

....

....

....

....

....

....

....

....

....

....

....

Score   / 30

WRITING TO ARGUE AND PERSUADE   Writing

Total score   / 35

How well did you do?   ✗ 0–10 **Try again**   11–20 **Getting there**   21–25 **Good work**   26–35 **Excellent!** ✓

Writing to advise

A

Choose just one answer, a, b, c or d/true or false.

1 Which of the following is not a
modal verb? **(1 mark)**

a) should ☐

b) may ☐

c) am ☐

d) could ☐

2 Opinions would not be used when
writing to advise. **(1 mark)**

true/false

3 Advice texts are often written in **(1 mark)**

a) 1st person ☐

b) 2nd person ☐

c) 3rd person ☐

d) 4th person ☐

4 In advice texts rhetorical questions
might be used to **(1 mark)**

a) find out information ☐

b) make a persuasive point ☐

c) give an answer ☐

d) introduce an idea ☐

5 Advice texts use imperative verbs. **(1 mark)**

true/false

Score /5

B

Use the space below to complete a plan for the writing task in Section C.

Although this section doesn't carry a score, it will help you to score higher marks in Section C.

Use this space to record the main points of advice you will give.

....

....

....

Use this space to record any key language features you will use.

....

....

....

....

Use this space to note down the presentation and layout features you will use.

....

....

....

....

C

Your answer should respond to each of the bullet points. You should spend about 40 minutes writing. Continue your writing on a separate sheet if necessary.

1 **Write an advice leaflet for teenagers on the subject of leading a healthy lifestyle.**

You could write about:

- smoking, drugs and alcohol
- diet
- exercise
- benefits of a healthy lifestyle.

(30 marks)

....

....

....

....

....

....

....

....

....

....

....

....

....

....

....

....

....

....

Score   / 30

Total score   / 35

How well did you do?   0–7 Try again   8–11 Getting there   12–16 Good work   17–25 Excellent! ✓

For more help on this topic see KS3 English Success Guide pages 56-57.

Writing to inform and explain

A

Choose just one answer, a, b, c or d/true or false.

1 Information texts are usually written in the first person. (1 mark)

true/false

2 Information and explanation texts are usually written in the present tense. (1 mark)

true/false

3 Explanation texts use logical connectives. Which of the following is *not* a logical connective? (1 mark)

a) because ☐

b) as a result of ☐

c) however ☐

d) firstly ☐

4 Which of the following sentence types do information texts use? (1 mark)

a) mostly complex ☐

b) mostly simple ☐

c) simple and compound ☐

d) compound and complex ☐

5 Explanation texts sometimes use the passive voice. Which of the following doesn't use the passive voice? (1 mark)

a) The window was broken. ☐

b) John broke the window. ☐

c) The window was broken by John. ☐

d) The window was broken accidentally. ☐

Score   / 5

B

Use the space below to complete a plan for the writing task in Section C.

Although this section doesn't carry a score, it will help you to score higher marks in Section C.

Use this space to brainstorm information about teenage fashion.

Make brief notes to explain why different people choose different styles.

Explanation: ....

....

....

....

KS3
Success

English

Answers

Pages 8–9

A
1. d
2. b
3. a
4. c
5. b

B
1. Sample answers include: 'Kingshaw got up and flapped his arms' – he doesn't like the crow, it makes him uneasy and he wants it to go away 'Stupid to be scared . . . bird do?' – he is angry with himself for being frightened. **(4 marks for 2 examples and explanations)**
2. a) They are very short.
   b) It creates tension, fear and a feeling of breathlessness. **(3 marks)**

C

Marks will be awarded as follows: **1–2 (below Level 4)** marks for a simple, generalised comment which relates to just one bullet point or repeats the prompts. **3–4 marks (Level 4)** for an answer which supports general comment about one bullet point with detail from the text. **5–6 marks (Level 5)** for an answer which supports general comment with detail from the text and addresses all bullet points. **7–8 marks (Level 6)** for an answer which addresses all of the bullet points, making specific comments supported by explanation and a range of detail from the text. **9–10 marks (Level 7)** for an answer which does all of the above, focusing on aspects of language and/or structure and giving a personal response.

Pages 12–13

A
1. a
2. a
3. c
4. d
5. b

B
1. a) 'it', 'she/her' **(2 marks)**
   b) 'Sample answers include: it makes Catherine Linton seem inhuman and it shows that the narrator doesn't feel any sympathy for her. **(2 marks for 2 correct points)**
2. Atmosphere: frightening and ghostly. **(1 mark)**
   Words and phrases: sample answers include 'ice-cold hand', 'horror of nightmare', 'terror and doleful cry'. **(2 marks for 4 words/phrases from the list)**

C

See answers for pages 8–9 C.

Pages 16–17

A
1. a
2. b
3. d
4. c
5. b

B
1. Exclamation and question marks **(1 mark)** indicate that they are shouting and there is a lot of disagreement. **(1 mark)**
2. Because Billy is so thin and dirty, he looks like a Jewish child from a concentration camp; the Jews were gassed in mass showers and Billy is running towards the shower; Billy resembles a Jew, so the bully, Mr Sugden, is compared to a Nazi. **(2 marks)**
3. Sample answers include: The phrases 'hands closed into fists' and 'lashed his body around' **(1 mark for 2 words or phrases)** describe violent actions and make him seem like a boxer. **(2 marks for two points)**

C

See answers for pages 8–9 C.

Pages 20–21

A
1. d
2. c
3. b
4. a
5. b

B
1. 4, 2, 1, 3 **(1 mark)**

2. Sample answers include: 'The cold bites through your coat' – makes it sound like he's being attacked; 'The darkening garden watches' – even though he is alone, he is being watched; 'The bushes hold their breath' – suggests they are waiting for something sinister to happen. **(4 marks for 2 examples and explanations)**
3. Use of full stops creates a pause after each instruction which makes it seem tense. The line is end stopped with a full stop, creating further emphasis on the three definite instructions. **(2 marks one for each comment)**

C

See answers for pages 8–9 C.

Pages 22–23

A
1. c
2. d
3. b
4. c
5. d

B
1. Sample answers include: 'green spears' – creates the idea of the nettles as a weapon; 'regiment of spite' – gives the idea that there are lots of them and they are organised like a cruel army; 'tall recruits' – this gives the idea that the new nettles are new members of the original enemy army that hurt his son. **(4 marks for 2 metaphors and explanations)**
2. As the nettles have regrown he may be stung and hurt again. His son would be physically or emotionally hurt by other things in the future. As a father, no matter how hard he tries, he can't protect his son from being hurt. **(2 marks)**
3. 'busy' **(1 mark)**

C

See answers for pages 8–9 C.

Pages 26–27

A
1. d
2. b
3. a
4. c
5. c

B
1. Mealtimes; emphasises discrimination in the system; 'whereas, our mealies were served straight' (other food quotations are acceptable). **(3 marks)**
2. Sample answers include: Temporal connective: 'After inspection', 'For lunch', 'Precisely at 4.30'. Focus on individuals, etc.: 'the guards would yell', 'We were required to', 'Common-law prisoners used to'. **(2 marks for 1 example from each list)**
3. Sample answers include: 'Val in! Val in!' – the English is given in brackets; *phuzamandla* – an explanation is given after the word 'which means'. **(2 marks for 1 example and explanation)**

C

See answers for pages 8–9 C.

Pages 30–31

A
1. d
2. b
3. a
4. c
5. d

B
1. Rhetorical question – it shows there has been some confusion about this and there are many possible answers **(2 marks 1 for technique and 1 for explanation)**
2. This is an information text so the sentences are usually quite straightforward and the main punctuation marks used are commas and full stops. Brackets are used to give additional information, provide dates or figures and give abbreviations. In the 'Flags' section the information is more complicated and here the punctuation is more advanced. For example – there are a number of possible reasons for the name of the Union Flag and these are separated by semi-colons. **(3 marks)**
3. Sample answers include: Temporal –'In mid-2003', 'Every ten years', 'Since the 17th century'; Logical – 'for instance' **(2 marks)**

C

See answers for pages 8–9 C.

Pages 34–35

A
1. c
2. b
3. d
4. b
5. c

B
1. Sample answers include: 'in fact', 'to my mind', 'In my opinion'. **(1 mark for 2 from list)**
2. Rhetorical question – it raises questions in the readers' minds and makes them think for themselves about their own response. **(2 marks)**
3. Sample answers include: adolescent obesity – lack of exercise; poor emotional and communication development – miss out on playing games, listening to stories and interacting with other children. **(4 marks for 2 examples and explanations)**

C
1. **Sample answers include:** Britain / British citizens – repeated throughout this section to emphasise the fact that British people were directly involved in the September 11 tragedy and to show that is a strong reason to take military action; Attacks – this is repeated several times and introduces the idea that military action is a necessary defence and to promote the idea that the US and Britain are not starting something they are responding to an attack; All – this word is used twice to show that all people can be united against terrorism regardless of nationality or religion; We / us – these personal pronouns are used repeatedly to try to unite the British people with Tony Blair and the Government against al-Qaeda.
2. Marks will be awarded as follows: **1–2 marks (below Level 4)** for a simple, generalised comment which relates to just one bullet point or repeats the prompts; **3 marks (Level 4)** for an answer which supports general comment about one bullet point detail from the text; **4 marks (Level 5)** for an answer which supports general comment with detail from the text and addresses all bullet points; **5 marks (Level 6)** for an answer which addresses all of the bullet points, making specific comments supported by explanation and a range of detail from the text; **6 marks (Level 7)** for an answer which does all of the above, focusing on aspects of language and/or structure and giving a personal response.

Pages 38–39

A
1. c
2. c
3. b
4. d
5. a

B
1. Imperative; this section is giving instructions and recipes, it tells you what to do rather than making suggestions. **(2 marks)**
2. Sample answers include: Pictures – make the leaflet look bright and inviting, shows examples of how you can present food; Headings – break up the text and draw attention to important points; Bullet points – get the information across in a quick and simple manner. **(2 marks for 2 examples and explanations)**
3. Fast food is usually associated with junk food. However, instead of telling parents not to feed their children fast food, the leaflet highlights the fact that healthy treats can be just as quick and easy to provide. This keeps the tone of the leaflet positive. It acknowledges the fact that parents don't always have a lot of time, and provides advice on how to incorporate healthy snacks into a child's diet without spending a long time preparing them. **(3 marks)**

C
See answers for pages 42–43 C.

Pages 40–41

A
1. d
2. c
3. false
4. true
5. d

C
The following mark scheme should be used to assess your writing.

A: Sentence structure/punctuation and text organisation

A1
Sentences are mainly simple or compound. Parts of sentences and ideas are linked mostly by conjunctions (e.g. 'and', 'then'). Full stops and capital letters are used with accuracy. Paragraphs may show obvious divisions, as given in task. **(1 mark)**

A2
Sentences are varied; relative clauses, such as those using 'who' and 'which', are used. Pronouns are generally used consistently, as

are tenses. Paragraphs are used appropriately with some sequencing and ordering of detail. **(2–3 marks)**

A3
Compound and complex sentences are used, with phrases and clauses building up relevant detail. Qualifying words (e.g. 'completely') are used to convey precise meaning. Pronouns and tenses are used consistently. Punctuation is used correctly. Paragraphs are used appropriately with sequencing of detail. **(4–5 marks)**

A4
A range of grammatical structures (such as adverbials) are used to vary the focus of sentences. A range of punctuation is used correctly; sometimes to create effects. Paragraphs are varied in structure and length in order to reflect the content of the writing. **(6 marks)**

B: Composition and effect

B1
The description shows some awareness of the reader. Simple devices such as repetition are used to signal key features of person/object described. Although there is relevant content, there is uneven coverage of the prompts given in the question. **(1–2 marks)**

B2
The description makes attempts to engage the reader's interest. Some stylistic devices are used to reinforce the meaning of the piece, such as patterning. The topic is covered adequately, but the description is unimaginative and formulaic. **(3–5 marks)**

B3
The writing engages the reader's interest. There is a secure sense of purpose in the description. The setting is developed, and various devices are used to communicate meaning. A coherent viewpoint is presented via reflection on the description and narrative. **(6–8 marks)**

B4
The description is well written and convincing throughout. The writing engages the reader's interest. A full range of appropriate details and ideas is included. The viewpoint of the writer is consistently maintained. There is a good balance between description and narrative in the piece of writing. **(9–10 marks)**

C: Spelling

C1
Simple words are usually accurate. **(1 mark)**

C2
Simple and polysyllabic words are generally accurate. **(2 marks)**

C3
Words with complex but regular patterns are generally accurate. **(3 marks)**

C4
Virtually all spelling, including complex irregular words, is correct. **(4 marks)**

Pages 42–43

A
1. c
2. a
3. b
4. false
5. false

C
The following mark scheme should be used to assess your writing.

A: Sentence structure and punctuation

A1
Ideas and sentences are mostly linked using conjunctions such as 'and', 'but' and 'when'. Sentences are mainly compound, and within them sentence subjects and verbs are frequently repeated. Full stops, capital letters, question marks and exclamation marks are used to demarcate sentences, mostly accurately. **(1 mark)**

A2
Sentences are varied; relative clauses, such as those using 'who' and 'which', are used. Subordinating conjunctions, such as 'if' and 'because', develop reasons and emphasis. Commas are used within sentences, mainly with accuracy. **(2–3 marks)**

A3

Compound and complex sentences are used. Phrases and clauses build up detail and give information. Suggestions are given using modal verbs such as 'can' and 'would'. A variety of punctuation is used with accuracy. Different types of sentence including exclamations, commands and questions add interest and variety. **(4–5 marks)**

A4

Shades of meaning are expressed through the use of a range of grammatical structures such as adverbials and impersonal openings. A range of punctuation is used with accuracy; this is sometimes used to create deliberate effects, such as bullets, parentheses, etc. **(6–7 marks)**

A5

Sentence structure is varied as appropriate. Simple sentences are used effectively and contrasts achieve particular effects or emphasis (e.g. past/present tense and active/passive voice). Punctuation is used with accuracy to clarify meaning, avoid ambiguity and vary pace. **(8 marks)**

B: Text structures and organisation

B1

Ideas are linked mainly through topic. Points may be listed in no particular order of importance. Paragraphs may be used to show obvious divisions. **(1 mark)**

B2

Paragraphs generally open with the main idea and contain examples or illustrations. **(2–3 marks)**

B3

Paragraphs are logically sequenced. There is a sense of introduction and conclusion. Paragraphs of different lengths are used to emphasise ideas used for persuasion or to create feelings of tension or excitement. Speech is paragraphed correctly. **(4–5 marks)**

B4

Detailed content is organised well within and between paragraphs. Some connectives are used to show logical relationships ('on the other hand'). The introduction and conclusion to persuasion and argument contribute to the persuasiveness of the text. The structure of narrative writing is controlled through paragraph length and organisation. **(6–7 marks)**

B5

Paragraphs are varied in length to help control ideas. Cohesion of the text is reinforced by the use of a range of linking devices (adverbials, connectives). Paragraph structure is varied to create impact and develop ideas. **(8 marks)**

C: Composition and effect

C1

The given form of the writing shows some awareness of the reader. There is some relevant content but possibly uneven coverage. **(1–2 marks)**

C2

Writing is generally lively and attempts to interest the reader. A sense of purpose is shown in the content of persuasive writing and some reasons are given for ideas and opinions. In narrative writing the plot structure is clear and is balanced with some description. **(3–5 marks)**

C3

Writing is detailed and gives clear reasons for opinions. It engages the reader's interest. A range of imaginative vocabulary is used to describe people and objects. **(6–8 marks)**

C4

In persuasion and argument a range of persuasive devices is used such as repetition, humour and a consideration of the reader's needs and position. The writer's viewpoint is maintained with consistency. In narrative writing imagery is used in description and alternative narrative structures are explored. **(9–11 marks)**

C5

The tone and content of writing is appropriate and well judged. Writing seeks and achieves deliberate interaction with the reader. Narrative writing shows control and development of characters and settings. **(12–14 marks)**

Pages 44–45

A
1. false
2. b
3. c
4. b
5. a

C
See answers for pages 42–43.

Pages 46-47

A
1. c
2. false
3. b
4. d
5. true

C
See answers for pages 42–43

Pages 48–49

A
1. false
2. true
3. d
4. c
5. b

C
See answers for pages 42–43.

Pages 50–51

A
1. b
2. true
3. b
4. d
5. true

C
See answers for pages 42–43.

Pages 56–57

A
1. d
2. c
3. b
4. c
5. d

B
1. Juliet is confused because she thinks Romeo is dead at first. This happens because the nurse doesn't mention any names just repeats 'he's dead, he's dead!'. Juliet assumes the nurse is talking about Romeo and the nurse doesn't correct her, instead she goes on to repeat Romeo's name. This is because she can't believe he has killed Tybalt, but Juliet thinks it's because he's killed himself. The nurse then goes on to describe the body and the wounds but still doesn't make it clear who is dead. She doesn't mention Tybalt until line 61. Juliet thinks that both men are dead at this point. It is not until lines 69–70 that the nurse explains very clearly what has happened 'Tybalt is gone and Romeo banished!' This may be because the nurse is so upset that she can't think clearly. This is also very like the nurse's style of speech in other parts of the play and isn't the first time Juliet has been kept waiting for information. **(5 marks)**
2. Sample answers include: 'dove-feathered raven', 'fiend angelical', 'damned saint'. The list of oxymorons highlights Juliet's deep confusion and conflicting emotions. She feels torn by her love for Romeo and her love for her family. She accuses Romeo of seeming beautiful and virtuous but acting in a vile and destructive way. **(1 mark for example, 1 mark for explanation)**

C
Some guidance about what is required to achieve each level is shown below. It is not specific to any of the plays you may have studied.

To achieve level 3: a simple retelling of the scenes; some basic features of language identified but no comment; some personal response to scenes but no recognition of Shakespeare's purpose; some recognition of the social or historical context of the play.

To achieve level 4: a few simple comments about the characters; answer still focuses on retelling the scenes; some basic features of language identified with simple comment about Shakespeare's choices; simple comments show awareness of Shakespeare's purpose in the scenes; simple comments on the way social and historical context of the play informs meaning.

To achieve level 5: answer displays a good level of understanding of the characters and their motivation; comments are supported by reference to the text; various features of language identified with explanation and comment showing awareness of the effects of Shakespeare's choices; Shakespeare's purpose and viewpoint clearly identified; some explanation of the way context informs meaning.

To achieve level 6: a focused answer with a degree of exploration of the text; detailed commentary displays understanding of characters, motivation and relationships; detailed explanation of how language is used and how this contributes to character and atmosphere; references to the text are appropriate and relevant and provide evidence of understanding Shakespeare's view point and purpose and the effect this has on the reader; some detailed discussion of the impact of context on meaning.

To achieve level 7: a full answer showing detailed knowledge of the text and the characters; sustained focus on the requirements of the question; detailed and precise analysis of how language contributes to the exploration of characters, motivation, relationships and themes; some evaluative comment about the way Shakespeare's viewpoint and purpose is established and sustained; comments show an appreciation of how specific devices and techniques create effects on the reader/audience; some analysis of the relationship between context and meaning.

Pages 58–59
A
1. a
2. b
3. c
4. c
5. c
B
1. Image – A ship being wrecked in a storm; Juliet – her body (the ship) is being wrecked by the storm of tears it shows us she is very upset; Capulet – he feels very sorry for his daughter and hates to see her so upset, perhaps he thinks she is too upset. **(3 marks)**
2. He talks about Juliet in the third person. He asks lots of questions which suggests he can't believe she dares to be disobedient. **(2 marks)**
3. Sample answers include: 'green-sickness carrion' – shows the strength of his feeling as this means rotting meat that would be eaten by scavengers, it shows his intention to disown her if she doesn't obey; 'young baggage' – shows the strength of his feeling as baggage can easily be thrown away, it also de-personalises her and makes her seem like a object with no feelings. **(1 mark for example, 1 mark for explanation)**
C
See guidance for pages 56–57.

Pages 64–65
A
1. c
2. b
3. d
4. a
5. c
B
1. Sample answers: a) His brother Jaques is allowed to be educated but he isn't; b) the horses get better care and attention than he does; c) he has to eat with the 'hinds' (farm labourers) **(1 mark for each reason)**
2. Sample answers: they call each other sir in sarcastic or disrespectful tones; Oliver accuses Orlando of spoiling things 'What mar you then, sir?'; they nearly have a fight; Oliver calls Orlando a villain. **(1 mark for each reason)**
3. He sees Orlando as beginning to cause trouble for him and he needs to find a way to 'get rid of him'; he is beginning to plot ways to cause harm to Orlando. **(1 mark for each suggestion)**
C
See guidance for pages 56–57

Page 66–67
A
1. a
2. b
3. d
4. b
5. a
B
1. He is listing all the good qualities that Orlando has 'gentle, strong and valiant'. But questioning why he has to be this way, 'Why are you virtuous'. He suggests that it is dangerous to have these qualities in Oliver's court because it makes other people like him, which causes Oliver to hate him. He worries that these good qualities will bring him to harm 'What is comely / Envenoms him that bears it!' **(3 marks)**
2. He says he would rather stay and face his murderous brother than leave and have to beg or be a thief in order to survive. This shows that he is brave and noble and doesn't want to act immorally to save himself. **(2 marks)**
3. Orlando describes himself as a 'rotten tree' and says he will not bear 'blossom' no matter how well Adam looks after him 'In lieu of all thy pains and husbandry'. It shows that Orlando sees

himself as unlucky and that no matter how good a servant Adam may be he can't make good things happen for Orlando and so he won't be rewarded for his efforts. **(2 marks)**
C
See guidance for pages 56–57

Pages 72–73
A
1. a
2. c
3. b
4. d
5. d
B
1. He says they torment him for every little thing: 'For every trifle are they set upon me'; he lists a range of torments: 'Sometime like apes', 'Their pricks at my footfall', 'hiss me into madness'; he hides: 'I'll fall flat'. **(1 mark for each reason with supporting quotation)**
2. He wants to tame him and make money out of him. **(1 mark)**
3. Trinculo talks about how bad he smells: 'a very ancient and fishlike smell . . . not-of-the-newest poor-John' and says he has legs and fins, which gives the impression that he doesn't look or smell human. Stephano repeatedly uses the words 'devil' and 'monster'; he thinks Caliban has four legs and two voices. Both of them think of ways they could make money from Caliban as a 'freak show'. **(2 marks for each point with quotation)**
C
See answers for pages 8–9 C.

Pages 74–75
A
1. b
2. c
3. d
4. b
5. a
B
1. He says the island will 'totter' or fall apart if all the people have the same intelligence as them ('be brained like us'). This shows he thinks that they are not very clever. **(1 mark for each part of answer)**
2. Stephano: 'servant monster', always refers to him as 'my', offers to make him standard-bearer, 'my subject', tells Caliban to kneel. **(1 mark for two examples from the list)** Caliban: 'Let me lick thy shoe', 'noble lord', 'my lord', 'my valiant master', 'I'll serve thee'. **(1 mark for two examples from the list)**
3. Hang him for mutiny, knock his teeth out for interrupting the story, beat him for interrupting Caliban. **(1 mark for each threat)**
C
See answers for pages 8–9 C.

Pages 76–77
A
1. c
2. d
3. b
4. c
5. b
B
1. Accommodation, committed, strawberries, separate, definite, churches, leaves, possible, successful, beautiful. **(1 mark for each)**
2. monkeys, boys **(1 mark)** factories, babies, tries. **(1 mark)**
3. If a word ends in a vowel and then y, just add an s. If a word ends in a consonant and y, change the y to an i and add es. **(1 mark)**
C
1. a) stepped; b) disappeared; c) quickly; d) caught; e) shelves; f) seen; g) imagining. **(1 mark for each correct answer)**
2. there, through, We're, saw, sore, know, hear, knot. **(1 mark for each correct answer)**

Pages 78–79
A
1. d
2. c
3. c
4. c
5. a
B
1. I went to the shop and (I) bought a chocolate bar. (The use of 'I' in the second clause is optional.) **(1 mark)**
2. Due to track repairs, the trains were late **OR** The Trains, due to track repairs, were late. **(1 mark for moving the clause, 1 mark for correct punctuation)**

3. The teacher, filled with despair, marked the exam papers. **(1 mark for embedding the clause, 1 mark for correct punctuation)**
4. Don't, who's (who is), couldn't, doesn't, Joanne's bag, the girls' bags (plural), the girl's bag (singular), the poet's writing (singular). **(1 mark for each)**

C

1. a) time, topic, talk. b) 2: When John stopped yelling…
   3: Moments later… 4: "Are you ok…" **(1 mark for each correct answer)**
2. a) When the rope snapped, the climber, who was very frightened, fell and broke his leg.
   b) 'Can I go out tonight Mum?' asked Alison.
   c) When the alarm rang, the workers left the building calmly.
   d) 'Gosh!' exclaimed the woman. 'I didn't see you there.'
   (2 marks for each correct answer)

Practice Test Paper 1
Reading, pages 81–91

1. Scrap of beef: feeds it to the hawk; swivel: attaches it to the jesses; leash: feeds it through the swivel or ties it around his glove. **(1 mark for complete answer)**
2. Hang upside down from the glove. **(1 mark)**
3. Sample answers include: he approaches slowly – this shows that he knows how to move without frightening the hawk; he chants her name softly – this shows he knows how to calm her down; he attaches the leash and ties it around his finger – he knows how to use the leash and jesses and he understands the importance of keeping everything secure so that the hawk cannot fly away. **(4 marks for 2 examples and explanations)**
4. He isn't sure whether Billy is joking or being serious; he wants Billy to think that he understands it's a joke and that he isn't scared. **(2 marks)**
5. **1 mark** for a simple, generalised comment which relates to just one bullet point or repeats the prompts;
   2 marks for an answer which supports general comment about one bullet point with detail from the text;
   3 marks for an answer which supports general comment with detail from the text and addresses all bullet points;
   4 marks for an answer which addresses all of the bullet points, making specific comments supported by explanation and a range of detail from the text;
   5–6 marks for an answer which does all of the above, focusing on aspects of language and/or structure and giving a personal response.
6. See answer to question 5.
7. Sample answers include: 'the reef gradually dipped' – the underwater landscape invites the diver to move slowly, the use of the word gradually suggests slow movement; 'its edges were rippling softly' – a ripple is a very slight movement of water and used with the word softly this makes you think that the movement must be slow otherwise waves would be created. **(2 marks for 1 example and explanation)**

8. It suggests that he is amazed and can hardly believe what he is seeing; 'transfixed' suggests that he is unable to move because he finds that experience so unexpected and unusual; 'realisation' suggests that he didn't know immediately what he was looking at. **(2 marks for 2 points from the list)**
9. 'single most . . . in my life' – he is full of admiration, by suggesting that he has never seen anything more beautiful he emphasises its beauty; 'Some people . . . fluid, and benign' – he wants to defend it from the cruel things other people have said, the range of adjectives he uses shows how incredible he thinks it is. **(4 marks)**
10. He is sorry to have had such a short time to look at the creature and believes he will never see it again but is thrilled and delighted to have seen it at all. **(2 marks)**
11. Sample answers include: at first he can only see a shadow moving above him – he doesn't know what it is; he describes himself as unprepared – this tells the reader that what happens next will be unusual or exciting; 'soared', 'rollercoaster' and 'sped off' create a feeling of speed, this is exciting because the manta ray seemed to be slow and gentle earlier. **(4 marks for a full answer)**
12. See answer to question 5.
13. To persuade people to give money; three different places to click to donate; tells you what your money will do; gives examples of how animals have been helped by the charity.
14. Sample answers: Fact – she had been wrapped in sellotape; Opinion – subjected to terrifying cruelty **(1 mark for each fact)**
15. personal pronouns you and we – creates the sense of team between the APO and the reader; makes it personalised; direct appeal to the reader to help; makes their help seem important. **(2 marks)**
16. See answer to question 5.

Practice Test Paper 2

Writing Section A, page 92
See answer for pages 42–43.

Writing Section B, page 93
See answer for pages 40–41.

Practice Test Paper 3
Shakespeare (Reading and understanding), page 94
See answer for pages 56–57.

ACKNOWLEDGEMENTS

The author and publisher are grateful to the copyright holders for permission to use quoted materials and photographs.

Published by Letts Educational
An imprint of HarperCollins*Publishers*
77–85 Fulham Palace Road
London W6 8JB

First published 2007

Telephone: 0844 576 8126
Fax: 0844 576 8131
Email: education@harpercollins.co.uk

ISBN: 9781844195435

Text © Kath Jordan 2007, 2010
Design and illustration © 2007, 2010 Letts Educational

British Library Cataloguing in Publication Data.
A CIP record of this book is available from the British Library.

Book Concept and Development: Helen Jacobs
Author: Kath Jordan
Editorial: Alan Worth and Marion Davies
Cover Design: Sarah Duxbury, Paul Oates and Paul Manning
Inside Concept Design: Starfish Design
Text Design, Layout and Editorial: MCS Publishing Services

C

Your answer should respond to each of the bullet points. You should spend about 20 minutes writing. Continue your writing on a separate sheet if necessary.

Fashions change very quickly and different groups of people like to wear different styles of clothing.

1 Write three paragraphs to inform the reader about current teenage fashion and explain why different people choose to follow different fashions.

You could write about:

• clothes and hairstyles

• the influence of music and celebrities on fashion.

Remember to write in the third person and present tense.

(20 marks)

....

....

....

....

....

....

....

....

....

....

....

....

....

....

....

....

....

....

....

....

....

Score   / 20

Total score   / 25

How well did you do?   ✗   0–7 **Try again**   8–11 **Getting there**   12–16 **Good work**   17–25 **Excellent!**   ✓

For more help on this topic see KS3 English Success Guide pages 52–53.

Writing to review, analyse, comment

A

Choose just one answer, a, b, c or d/true or false.

1 **A review should contain** (1 mark)

a) fact only ☐

b) fact and opinion ☐

c) opinion only ☐

d) opinion presented as fact ☐

2 **A review should explore the strengths and weaknesses of the piece being reviewed.** (1 mark)

true/false

3 **Comment and analysis texts should contain** (1 mark)

a) statements and explanations ☐

b) statements and explanations supported

by textual evidence ☐

c) long quotations without explanation ☐

d) unsupported opinions ☐

4 **Analysis texts should be written in the** (1 mark)

a) first person ☐

b) second person ☐

c) first and third person ☐

d) third person ☐

5 **Review texts can be written in the first or third person.** (1 mark)

true/false

Score / 5

B

Use the space below to complete a plan for the writing task in Section C.

Although this section doesn't carry a score, it will help you to score higher marks in Section C.

Make brief notes under the following headings:

Strengths

....

....

....

Weaknesses

....

....

....

Recommendations

....

....

....

....

C

Your answer should respond to each of the bullet points. You should spend about 20 minutes writing. Continue your writing on a separate sheet if necessary.

1 Write a brief review of a book you have read or a film you have seen recently. Write three paragraphs only.

You could include:

- information about the book/film
- the strengths of the book/film
- the weaknesses of the book/film
- your recommendations to other readers/viewers. (20 marks)

....

....

....

....

....

....

....

....

....

....

....

....

....

....

....

....

....

....

....

....

....

....

....

....

Score   / 20

Total score   / 25

How well did you do?   0–7 **Try again**   8–11 **Getting there**   12–16 **Good work**   17–25 **Excellent!** ✓

For more help on this topic see KS3 English Success Guide pages 58–59.

Romeo and Juliet

Read the two extracts from the play carefully and answer the questions that follow.

In this scene Juliet is waiting for Romeo to come to her that night, she knows nothing of the murders that have taken place. When the nurse brings news, she is devastated at first thinking Romeo is dead and then threatening to kill herself when she discovers Romeo has been banished.

Act III Scene 2

Enter JULIET

JULIET Gallop apace, you fiery-footed steeds,
   Towards Phoebus' lodging: such a wagoner
   As Phaethon would whip you to the west,
   And bring in cloudy night immediately.
   Spread thy close curtain, love-performing night,
   That runaway's eyes may wink and Romeo
   Leap to these arms, untalk'd of and unseen.
   Lovers can see to do their amorous rites
   By their own beauties; or, if love be blind,
   It best agrees with night. Come, civil night,   10
   Thou sober-suited matron, all in black,
   And learn me how to lose a winning match,
   Play'd for a pair of stainless maidenhoods:
   Hood my unmann'd blood, bating in my cheeks,
   With thy black mantle; till strange love, grown bold,
   Think true love acted simple modesty.
   Come, night; come, Romeo; come, thou day in
      night;
   For thou wilt lie upon the wings of night
   Whiter than new snow on a raven's back.
   Come, gentle night, come, loving, black-brow'd
      night,   20
   Give me my Romeo; and, when he shall die,
   Take him and cut him out in little stars,
   And he will make the face of heaven so fine
   That all the world will be in love with night
   And pay no worship to the garish sun.
   O, I have bought the mansion of a love,
   But not possess'd it, and, though I am sold,
   Not yet enjoy'd: so tedious is this day
   As is the night before some festival
   To an impatient child that hath new robes   30
   And may not wear them. O, here comes my
      nurse,

   And she brings news; and every tongue that
      speaks
   But Romeo's name speaks heavenly eloquence.

Enter Nurse, with cords

   Now, nurse, what news? What hast thou there?
      the cords
   That Romeo bid thee fetch?
NURSE Ay, ay, the cords.

Throws them down

JULIET Ay me! what news? why dost thou wring thy
      hands?
NURSE Ah weraday, he's dead, he's dead, he's
      dead!
   We are undone, lady, we are undone!
   Alack the day! he's gone, he's kill'd,
      he's dead!   40
JULIET Can heaven be so envious?
NURSE Romeo can,
   Though heaven cannot: O Romeo, Romeo!
   Who ever would have thought it? Romeo!
JULIET What devil art thou, that dost torment me
      thus?
   This torture should be roar'd in dismal hell.
   Hath Romeo slain himself? say thou but 'I,'
   And that bare vowel 'I' shall poison more
   Than the death-darting eye of cockatrice:
   I am not I, if there be such an I;   50
   Or those eyes shut, that make thee answer 'I.'
   If he be slain, say 'I'; or if not, no:
   Brief sounds determine of my weal or woe.
NURSE I saw the wound, I saw it with mine eyes,--
   God save the mark!--here on his manly breast:
   A piteous corse, a bloody piteous corse;
   Pale, pale as ashes, all bedaub'd in blood,

All in gore-blood; I swounded at the sight.

JULIET O, break, my heart! poor bankrupt, breakat once!

To prison, eyes, ne'er look on liberty! 60

Vile earth, to earth resign; end motion here;

And thou and Romeo press one heavy bier!

NURSE O Tybalt, Tybalt, the best friend I had!

O courteous Tybalt! honest gentleman!

That ever I should live to see thee dead!

JULIET What storm is this that blows so contrary?

Is Romeo slaughter'd, and is Tybalt dead?

My dear-loved cousin, and my dearer lord?

Then, dreadful trumpet, sound the general doom!

For who is living, if those two are gone? 70

NURSE Tybalt is gone, and Romeo banished;

Romeo that kill'd him, he is banished.

JULIET O God! did Romeo's hand shed Tybalt's blood?

NURSE It did, it did; alas the day, it did!

JULIET O serpent heart, hid with a flowering face!

Did ever dragon keep so fair a cave?

Beautiful tyrant! fiend angelical!

Dove-feather'd raven! wolvish-ravening lamb!

Despised substance of divinest show!

Just opposite to what thou justly seem'st, 80

A damned saint, an honourable villain!

O nature, what hadst thou to do in hell,

When thou didst bower the spirit of a fiend

In moral paradise of such sweet flesh?

Was ever book containing such vile matter

So fairly bound? O that deceit should dwell

In such a gorgeous palace!

NURSE There's no trust,

No faith, no honesty in men; all perjured,

All forsworn, all naught, all dissemblers. 90

Ah, where's my man? give me some aqua vitae:

These griefs, these woes, these sorrows make me old.

Shame come to Romeo!

JULIET Blister'd be thy tongue

For such a wish! he was not born to shame:

Upon his brow shame is ashamed to sit;

For 'tis a throne where honour may be crown'd

Sole monarch of the universal earth.

O, what a beast was I to chide at him!

NURSE Will you speak well of him that kill'd your cousin? 100

JULIET Shall I speak ill of him that is my husband?

Ah, poor my lord, what tongue shall smooth thy name,

When I, thy three-hours wife, have mangled it?

But, wherefore, villain, didst thou kill my cousin?

That villain cousin would have kill'd my husband:

Back, foolish tears, back to your native spring;

Your tributary drops belong to woe,

Which you, mistaking, offer up to joy.

My husband lives, that Tybalt would have slain;

And Tybalt's dead, that would have slain my husband: 110

All this is comfort; wherefore weep I then?

Some word there was, worser than Tybalt's death,

That murder'd me: I would forget it fain;

But, O, it presses to my memory,

Like damned guilty deeds to sinners' minds:

'Tybalt is dead, and Romeo--banished;'

That 'banished,' that one word 'banished,'

Hath slain ten thousand Tybalts. Tybalt's death

Was woe enough, if it had ended there:

Or, if sour woe delights in fellowship 120

And needly will be rank'd with other griefs,

Why follow'd not, when she said 'Tybalt's dead,'

Thy father, or thy mother, nay, or both,

Which modern lamentations might have moved?

But with a rear-ward following Tybalt's death,

'Romeo is banished,' to speak that word,

Is father, mother, Tybalt, Romeo, Juliet,

All slain, all dead. 'Romeo is banished!'

There is no end, no limit, measure, bound,

In that word's death; no words can that woe sound. 130

Where is my father, and my mother, nurse?

NURSE Weeping and wailing over Tybalt's corse:

Will you go to them? I will bring you thither.

JULIET Wash they his wounds with tears: mine shall be spent,

When theirs are dry, for Romeo's banishment.

Take up those cords: poor ropes, you are beguiled,

Both you and I; for Romeo is exiled:
He made you for a highway to my bed;
But I, a maid, die maiden-widowed.
Come, cords, come, nurse; I'll to my wedding-bed; 140
And death, not Romeo, take my maidenhead!

NURSE Hie to your chamber: I'll find Romeo
To comfort you: I wot well where he is.
Hark ye, your Romeo will be here at night:
I'll to him; he is hid at Laurence' cell.

JULIET O, find him! give this ring to my true knight,
And bid him come to take his last farewell.

Exeunt

In this extract, having spent the night with Romeo in secret, Juliet refuses her father's instruction to marry Paris. Lord Capulet is furious and threatens to disown her if she will not obey. Her mother refuses to help her.

Act III Scene 5 lines 126-169

CAPULET	When the sun sets, the air doth drizzle dew;
	But for the sunset of my brother's son
	It rains downright.
	How now! a conduit, girl? what, still in tears?
	Evermore showering? In one little body 130
	Thou counterfeit'st a bark, a sea, a wind;
	For still thy eyes, which I may call the sea,
	Do ebb and flow with tears; the bark thy body is,
	Sailing in this salt flood; the winds, thy sighs;
	Who, raging with thy tears, and they with them,
	Without a sudden calm, will overset
	Thy tempest-tossed body. How now, wife!
	Have you deliver'd to her our decree?
LADY CAPULET	Ay, sir; but she will none, she gives you thanks.
	I would the fool were married to her grave! 140
CAPULET	Soft! take me with you, take me with you, wife.
	How! will she none? doth she not give us thanks?
	Is she not proud? doth she not count her blest,
	Unworthy as she is, that we have wrought
	So worthy a gentleman to be her bridegroom?
JULIET	Not proud, you have; but thankful, that you have:
	Proud can I never be of what I hate;
	But thankful even for hate, that is meant love.
CAPULET	How now, how now, chop-logic! What is this?
	'Proud,' and 'I thank you,' and 'I thank you not;' 150
	And yet 'not proud,' mistress minion, you,
	Thank me no thankings, nor, proud me no prouds,
	But fettle your fine joints 'gainst Thursday next,
	To go with Paris to Saint Peter's Church,
	Or I will drag thee on a hurdle thither.

	Out, you green-sickness carrion! out, you baggage!
	You tallow-face!
LADY CAPULET	Fie, fie! what, are you mad?
JULIET	Good father, I beseech you on my knees,
	Hear me with patience but to speak a word
CAPULET	Hang thee, young baggage! disobedient wretch!
	I tell thee what: get thee to church o' Thursday,
	Or never after look me in the face:
	Speak not, reply not, do not answer me;
	My fingers itch. Wife, we scarce thought us blest
	That God had lent us but this only child;
	But now I see this one is one too much,
	And that we have a curse in having her:
	Out on her, hilding!

160

Romeo and Juliet: questions

All of the questions that follow relate to Act III Scene 2

A

Choose just one answer, a, b, c or d.

1 Juliet's speech at the beginning of the scene is   (1 mark)

   a) an aside ☐

   b) a sonnet ☐

   c) a solo ☐

   d) a soliloquy ☐

2 The nurse brings news of whose death to Juliet?   (1 mark)

   a) Romeo ☐

   b) her father ☐

   c) Tybalt ☐

   d) Mercutio ☐

3 'A damned saint, an honourable villain' are examples of   (1 mark)

   a) personification ☐

   b) oxymoron ☐

   c) metaphor ☐

   d) euphemism ☐

4 When Juliet finds out Romeo has been banished she threatens to   (1 mark)

   a) kill the nurse ☐

   b) kill her family ☐

   c) kill herself ☐

   d) kill Friar Laurence ☐

5 The nurse promises to   (1 mark)

   a) kill Romeo ☐

   b) help Juliet to run away ☐

   c) help Juliet kill herself ☐

   d) send Romeo to her that night ☐

Score   / 5

B

Answer all parts of all questions.

1 Re-read line 38 'Ah weraday, he's dead...' to line 72 'Romeo that kill'd him, he is banished'. Explain why Juliet is confused by the nurse and why this might have happened.

Use evidence from the text to support your answer.   (5 marks)

....

....

....

....

....

2 Find an example of an oxymoron in Juliet's speech from line 75–87 and explain what all of the oxymorons in this speech reveal about how she is feeling.   (2 marks)

Example:...

Explanation: ....

Score   / 7

C

Your answer should respond to each of the bullet points.

1 **How does Shakespeare show Juliet's feelings for Romeo in this scene?**

You should write about:

• what she says before the nurse arrives

• how she reacts to the news of Tybalt's death and Romeo's banishment

• how she reacts to the nurse's poor opinion of Romeo   (10 marks)

....

....

....

....

....

....

....

....

....

....

....

....

....

....

....

....

....

....

....

....

....

....

....

Score   / 10

Total score   / 22

How well did you do?   ✗   0–6 **Try again**   7–10 **Getting there**   11–14 **Good work**   15–22 **Excellent!**   ✓

For more help on this topic see KS3 English Success Guide pages 66–75.

57

Romeo and Juliet

All of the questions that follow relate to Act III Scene 5

A Choose just one answer, a, b, c or d.

1 At the beginning of the extract Capulet thinks Juliet is crying because *(1 mark)*

a) Tybalt is dead ☐

b) she doesn't want to marry Paris ☐

c) Romeo is banished ☐

d) Mercutio is dead ☐

2 Why does Capulet become angry with Juliet? *(1 mark)*

a) she is married to Romeo ☐

b) she won't marry Paris ☐

c) she is rude to him ☐

d) she wants to go to church ☐

3 'I would the fool were married to her grave' is an example of *(1 mark)*

a) simile ☐

b) oxymoron ☐

c) dramatic irony ☐

d) humour ☐

4 What day is the wedding? *(1 mark)*

a) Sunday ☐

b) Tuesday ☐

c) Thursday ☐

d) Friday ☐

5 What does Capulet threaten to do if she refuses to do as she is told? *(1 mark)*

a) kill her ☐

b) put her in a nunnery ☐

c) disown her ☐

d) lock her away ☐

Score / 5

B Answer all parts of all questions.

1 What image does Capulet use to describe Juliet's tears at the beginning of this extract?

Explain what this suggests to us about how Juliet is feeling and how Capulet feels about his daughter at the beginning of the scene. *(3 marks)*

Image: ....

Juliet's feelings: ....

Capulet's feelings: ....

2 In lines 141–145, how does Shakespeare show that Capulet is beginning to get angry with Juliet? *(2 marks)*

....

....

3 Give an example of an insult Capulet uses against Juliet and explain its intended effect. *(2 marks)*

Insult: ....

Explanation: ....

....

Score / 7

C Your answer should respond to each of the bullet points.

1 **How does Shakespeare show the way Capulet's feelings for his daughter change in this extract?**

You should write about:

- his behaviour and language at the beginning of the extract
- what he says to his wife about Juliet
- how he speaks and behaves towards Juliet when he finds out she won't marry Paris   (10 marks)

....

....

....

....

....

....

....

....

....

....

....

....

....

....

....

....

....

....

....

....

....

....

....

Score   / 10

Total score   / 22

How well did you do?   0–6 **Try again**   7–10 **Getting there**   11–14 **Good work**   15–22 **Excellent!** ✓

For more help on this topic see KS3 English Success Guide pages 66–75.

59

As You Like It

Read the two extracts from the play carefully and answer the questions that follow.

In this scene Orlando complains to Adam that his older brother Oliver is treating him like a servant and refusing to follow their late father's wishes. Oliver is angered by Orlando's demands and a fight almost begins.

Act I, Scene 1, Lines 1–86

Enter ORLANDO *and* ADAM

ORLANDO	As I remember, Adam, it was upon this fashion	
	bequeathed me by will but poor a thousand crowns,	
	and, as thou sayest, charged my brother, on his	
	blessing, to breed me well: and there begins my	
	sadness. My brother Jaques he keeps at school, and	
	report speaks goldenly of his profit: for my part,	
	he keeps me rustically at home, or, to speak more	
	properly, stays me here at home unkept; for call you	
	that keeping for a gentleman of my birth, that	
	differs not from the stalling of an ox? His horses	10
	are bred better; for, besides that they are fair	
	with their feeding, they are taught their manage,	
	and to that end riders dearly hired: but I, his	
	brother, gain nothing under him but growth; for the	
	which his animals on his dunghills are as much	
	bound to him as I. Besides this nothing that he so	
	plentifully gives me, the something that nature gave	
	me his countenance seems to take from me: he lets	
	me feed with his hinds, bars me the place of a	
	brother, and, as much as in him lies, mines my	20
	gentility with my education. This is it, Adam, that	
	grieves me; and the spirit of my father, which I	
	think is within me, begins to mutiny against this	
	servitude: I will no longer endure it, though yet I	
	know no wise remedy how to avoid it.	
ADAM	Yonder comes my master, your brother.	
ORLANDO	Go apart, Adam, and thou shalt hear how he will shake me up. *Enter* OLIVER	
OLIVER	Now, sir! what make you here?	
ORLANDO	Nothing: I am not taught to make any thing.	
OLIVER	What mar you then, sir?	30
ORLANDO	Marry, sir, I am helping you to mar that which God	
	made, a poor unworthy brother of yours, with idleness.	
OLIVER	Marry, sir, be better employed, and be naught awhile.	
ORLANDO	Shall I keep your hogs and eat husks with them?	
	What prodigal portion have I spent, that I should	
	come to such penury?	
OLIVER	Know you where your are, sir?	

ORLANDO	O, sir, very well; here in your orchard.
OLIVER	Know you before whom, sir?
ORLANDO	Ay, better than him I am before knows me. I know
	you are my eldest brother; and, in the gentle
	condition of blood, you should so know me. The
	courtesy of nations allows you my better, in that
	you are the first-born; but the same tradition
	takes not away my blood, were there twenty brothers
	betwixt us: I have as much of my father in me as
	you; albeit, I confess, your coming before me is
	nearer to his reverence.
OLIVER	What, boy!
ORLANDO	Come, come, elder brother, you are too young in this.
OLIVER	Wilt thou lay hands on me, villain?
ORLANDO	I am no villein; I am the youngest son of Sir
	Rowland de Boys; he was my father, and he is thrice
	a villain that says such a father begot villains.
	Wert thou not my brother, I would not take this hand
	from thy throat till this other had pulled out thy
	tongue for saying so: thou hast railed on thyself.
ADAM	Sweet masters, be patient: for your father's
	remembrance, be at accord.
OLIVER	Let me go, I say.
ORLANDO	I will not, till I please: you shall hear me. My
	father charged you in his will to give me good
	education: you have trained me like a peasant,
	obscuring and hiding from me all gentleman-like
	qualities. The spirit of my father grows strong in
	me, and I will no longer endure it: therefore allow
	me such exercises as may become a gentleman, or
	give me the poor allottery my father left me by
	testament; with that I will go buy my fortunes.
OLIVER	And what wilt thou do? beg, when that is spent?
	Well, sir, get you in: I will not long be troubled
	with you; you shall have some part of your will: I
	pray you, leave me.
ORLANDO	I will no further offend you than becomes me for my good.
OLIVER	Get you with him, you old dog.
ADAM	Is 'old dog' my reward? Most true, I have lost my
	teeth in your service. God be with my old master!
	he would not have spoke such a word. *Exeunt* ORLANDO *and* ADAM
OLIVER	Is it even so? begin you to grow upon me? I will
	physic your rankness, and yet give no thousand
	crowns neither. Holla, Dennis! *Enter* DENNIS
DENNIS	Calls your worship?
OLIVER	Was not Charles, the duke's wrestler, here to speak with me?
DENNIS	So please you, he is here at the door and importunes access to you.
OLIVER	Call him in. *Exit* DENNIS
	'Twill be a good way; and to-morrow the wrestling is.

Exit

Act II Scene 3

In this scene Adam reveals Oliver's plot to kill Orlando and urges him to leave the court. Orlando says he would rather face his brother than become a beggar. Adam offers his life savings and faithful service. Orlando thanks Adam and agrees to leave.

Act II Scene 3

Enter ORLANDO *and* ADAM, *meeting*

ORLANDO	Who's there?	
ADAM	What, my young master? O, my gentle master!	
	O my sweet master! O you memory	
	Of old Sir Rowland! why, what make you here?	
	Why are you virtuous? why do people love you?	
	And wherefore are you gentle, strong and valiant?	
	Why would you be so fond to overcome	
	The bonny priser of the humorous duke?	
	Your praise is come too swiftly home before you.	
	Know you not, master, to some kind of men	10
	Their graces serve them but as enemies?	
	No more do yours: your virtues, gentle master,	
	Are sanctified and holy traitors to you.	
	O, what a world is this, when what is comely	
	Envenoms him that bears it!	
ORLANDO	Why, what's the matter?	
ADAM	O unhappy youth!	
	Come not within these doors; within this roof	
	The enemy of all your graces lives:	
	Your brother--no, no brother; yet the son--	20
	Yet not the son, I will not call him son	
	Of him I was about to call his father--	
	Hath heard your praises, and this night he means	
	To burn the lodging where you use to lie	
	And you within it: if he fail of that,	
	He will have other means to cut you off.	
	I overheard him and his practises.	
	This is no place; this house is but a butchery:	
	Abhor it, fear it, do not enter it.	
ORLANDO	Why, whither, Adam, wouldst thou have me go?	30
ADAM	No matter whither, so you come not here.	
ORLANDO	What, wouldst thou have me go and beg my food?	
	Or with a base and boisterous sword enforce	
	A thievish living on the common road?	
	This I must do, or know not what to do:	
	Yet this I will not do, do how I can;	
	I rather will subject me to the malice	
	Of a diverted blood and bloody brother.	
ADAM	But do not so. I have five hundred crowns,	
	The thrifty hire I saved under your father,	40

Which I did store to be my foster-nurse
When service should in my old limbs lie lame
And unregarded age in corners thrown:
Take that, and He that doth the ravens feed,
Yea, providently caters for the sparrow,
Be comfort to my age! Here is the gold;
And all this I give you. Let me be your servant:
Though I look old, yet I am strong and lusty;
For in my youth I never did apply
Hot and rebellious liquors in my blood,   50
Nor did not with unbashful forehead woo
The means of weakness and debility;
Therefore my age is as a lusty winter,
Frosty, but kindly: let me go with you;
I'll do the service of a younger man
In all your business and necessities.

ORLANDO O good old man, how well in thee appears
The constant service of the antique world,
When service sweat for duty, not for meed!
Thou art not for the fashion of these times,   60
Where none will sweat but for promotion,
And having that, do choke their service up
Even with the having: it is not so with thee.
But, poor old man, thou prunest a rotten tree,
That cannot so much as a blossom yield
In lieu of all thy pains and husbandry
But come thy ways; we'll go along together,
And ere we have thy youthful wages spent,
We'll light upon some settled low content.

ADAM Master, go on, and I will follow thee,   70
To the last gasp, with truth and loyalty.
From seventeen years till now almost fourscore
Here lived I, but now live here no more.
At seventeen years many their fortunes seek;
But at fourscore it is too late a week:
Yet fortune cannot recompense me better
Than to die well and not my master's debtor.

Exeunt

As You Like It: questions

All of the questions that follow relate to Act I Scene 1

A

Choose just one answer, a, b, c or d.

1 This extract is written in (1 mark)
a) blank verse ☐
b) rhyming couplets ☐
c) prose ☐
d) sonnet form ☐

2 Oliver is Orlando's (1 mark)
a) younger brother ☐
b) older brother ☐
c) father ☐
d) uncle ☐

3 Oliver calls Orlando a 'villain' and Orlando says he is not a 'villein'. This device is (1 mark)
a) alliteration ☐
b) an oxymoron ☐
c) irony ☐
d) a pun ☐

4 According to the will, what should Oliver be providing for Orlando? (1 mark)
a) proper education ☐
b) a job ☐
c) a wife ☐
d) land ☐

5 What is the name of the Duke's wrestler? (1 mark)
a) Adam ☐
b) Denis ☐
c) Charles ☐
d) Roland ☐

Score / 5

B

Answer all parts of all questions.

1 Identify three things that Orlando complains about in his first speech. (3 marks)

a) ....

b) ....

c) ....

2 Re-read the exchange between Oliver and Orlando beginning 'Now sir, what make you here?' and ending 'thou hast railed on thyself'. Give two ways you can tell they do not like each other. (2 marks)

a) ....

b) ....

3 What do Oliver's soliloquies at lines 79–81 and 86 reveal about his feelings towards Orlando? (2 marks)

....

....

Score / 7

Your answer should respond to each of the bullet points.

1 **How does Shakespeare present the character of Oliver in this scene?**

You should write about:

• what Orlando says about the way he is being treated by Oliver

• the way Oliver and Orlando speak to each other

• the way Oliver treats Adam

• what Oliver says in his soliloquies

(10 marks)

....

....

....

....

....

....

....

....

....

....

....

....

....

....

....

....

....

....

....

....

....

....

....

Score **/ 10**

AS YOU LIKE IT **Shakespeare**

Total score **/ 22**

How well did you do? ✗ 0–6 **Try again** 7–10 **Getting there** 11–14 **Good work** 15–22 **Excellent!** ✓

For more help on this topic see KS3 English Success Guide pages 66–75.

As You Like It: questions

All of the questions that follow relate to Act II Scene 3

A Choose just one answer, a, b, c or d.

1 **This scene is written in** (1 mark)

a) blank verse ☐

b) rhyming couplets ☐

c) prose ☐

d) sonnet form ☐

2 **Adam tells Orlando he should leave because** (1 mark)

a) Charles is plotting to kill him ☐

b) Oliver is plotting to kill him ☐

c) he has brought shame on his father's name ☐

d) Duke Frederick is plotting to kill him ☐

3 **Orlando doesn't want to leave the court because** (1 mark)

a) he is frightened ☐

b) he thinks he can make up with his brother ☐

c) he thinks Adam is trying to trick him ☐

d) he doesn't want to have to become a thief to survive ☐

4 **Orlando describes himself as 'a rotten tree'. This is** (1 mark)

a) a simile ☐

b) a metaphor ☐

c) personification ☐

d) an oxymoron ☐

5 **This scene ends with** (1 mark)

a) a rhyming couplet ☐

b) a rhyming triplet ☐

c) a joke ☐

d) a threat ☐

Score   / 5

B Answer all parts of all questions.

1 Re-read Adam's speech beginning 'What, my young master!' and ending 'Envenoms him that bears it!' Explain what he is saying about Orlando's character and how this is dangerous for him. Use quotations to support your answer. (3 marks)

....

....

....

2 How does Orlando respond to Adam's suggestion to leave the court and what does this reveal about his character? (2 marks)

....

....

3 How does Shakespeare extend the image of a 'rotten tree' in the lines that follow and explain how this shows how Orlando is feeling. (2 marks)

....

....

Score   / 7

Your answer should respond to each of the bullet points.

1 **How does Shakespeare demonstrate the loyalty and nobility of Adam the servant in this scene?**

You should write about:

- the way he speaks and behaves
- what he says about his youth
- the way Orlando treats him

(10 marks)

....

....

....

....

....

....

....

....

....

....

....

....

....

....

....

....

....

....

....

....

....

....

....

Score   / 10

Total score   / 22

How well did you do?   ✗   0–6 **Try again**   7–10 **Getting there**   11–14 **Good work**   15–22 **Excellent!** ✓

For more help on this topic see KS3 English Success Guide pages 66–75.

The Tempest

Read the two extracts from the play carefully and answer the questions that follow.

In this scene Caliban is complaining about Prospero. When he hears Trinculo, he hides fearing that he is one of Prospero's spirits. Trinculo is frightened of the weather and hides under Caliban's cloak. Stephano discovers Trinculo and they force Caliban to drink.

Act II Scene 2 lines 1–101

Enter CALIBAN, *with a burden of wood. A noise of thunder heard*

CALIBAN All the infections that the sun sucks up
From bogs, fens, flats, on Prosper fall, and make him
By inch-meal a disease. His spirits hear me,
And yet I needs must curse. But they'll nor pinch,
Fright me with urchin-shows, pitch me i'th'mire,
Nor lead me like a firebrand in the dark
Out of my way, unless he bid 'em; but
For every trifle are they set upon me,
Sometime like apes, that mow and chatter at me
And after bite me; then like hedgehogs, which 10
Lie tumbling in my barefoot way and mount
Their pricks at my footfall; sometime am I
All wound with adders, who with cloven tongues
Do hiss me into madness.

Enter TRINCULO

Lo, now lo!
Here comes a spirit of his, and to torment me
For bringing wood in slowly. I'll fall flat,
Perchance he will not mind me.
[*He lies down, and covers himself with a cloak*]
TRINCULO Here's neither bush, nor shrub to bear
off any weather at all, and another storm
brewing – I hear it sing i'th'wind. Yond same 20
black cloud, yond huge one, looks like a foul
bombard that would shed his liquor. If it
should thunder as it did before, I know not
where to hide my head. Yond same cloud
cannot choose but fall by pailfulls. [*Sees*
CALIBAN] What have we here – a man, or a
fish? Dead or alive? A fish, he smells like a
fish; a very ancient and fishlike smell; a kind
of, not-of-the-newest poor-John. A strange
fish. Were I in England now – as once I was –
and had but this fish painted, not a holiday-
fool there but would give a piece of silver.
There, would this monster make a man; any
strange beast there makes a man. When they 30
will not give a doit to relieve a lame beggar,
they will lay out ten to see a dead Indian.
Legged like a man – and his fins like arms.
Warm o'my troth! I do now let loose my
opinion, hold it no longer: this is no fish, but
an islander, that hath lately suffered by a
thunderbolt. [*Thunder*] Alas, the storm is
come again. My best way is to creep under his
gaberdine; there is no other shelter hereabout.
Misery acquaints a man with strange
bedfellows. I will here shroud till the dregs of
the storm be past.   40
[*He hides under* CALIBAN's *cloak*]

Enter STEPHANO [*carrying a bottle and*] *singing.*

STEPHANO I shall no more to sea, to sea, Here
shall I die ashore.
This is a very scurvy tune to sing at a man's
funeral. Well, here's my comfort. (*Drinks*)
(*Sings*) The master, the swabber, the boatswain
and I,
The gunner, and his mate,
Loved Mall, Meg, and Marian, and Margery,
But none of us cared for Kate.
For she had a tongue with a tang,   50
Would cry to a sailor, 'Go hang!'
She loved not the savour of tar nor of pitch,
Yet a tailor might scratch her where'er she did
itch.
Then to sea boys, and let her go hang!
This is a scurvy tune too; but here's my comfort.
(*Drinks*)

CALIBAN Do not torment me! O!

STEPHANO What's the matter? Have we devils here? Do you put tricks upon's with savages and men of Ind? Ha? I have not 'scaped drowning to be afeared now of your four legs. For it hath been said, 'As proper a man as ever went on four legs, cannot make him give ground'; and it shall be said so again, while Stephano breathes at' nostrils. 60

CALIBAN The spirit torments me! O!

STEPHANO This is some monster of the isle, with four legs, who hath got, as I take it, an ague. Where the devil should he learn our language? I will give him some relief if it be but for that. If I can recover him, and keep him tame, and get to Naples with him, he's a present for any emperor that ever trod on neat's leather.

CALIBAN Do not torment me, prithee! I'll bring my wood home faster.

STEPHANO He's in his fit now, and does not talk 70 after the wisest. He shall taste of my bottle. If he have never drunk wine afore, it will go near to remove his fit. If I can recover him, and keep him tame, I will not take too much for him; he shall pay for him that hath him, and that soundly.

CALIBAN Thou dost me yet but little hurt; thou wilt anon, I know it by thy trembling. Now Prosper works upon thee.

STEPHANO Come on your ways. Open your mouth; here is that which will give language to you, cat. Open your mouth; this will shake your shaking, I can tell you, and that soundly.

[CALIBAN *drinks and spits it out*]

You cannot tell who's your friend: open your 80 chops again.

[CALIBAN *drinks again*]

TRINCULO I should know that voice. It should be – but he is drowned, and these are devils. O defend me!

STEPHANO Four legs and two voices; a most delicate monster! His forward voice now is to speak well of his friend; his backward voice is to utter foul speeches, and to detract. If all the wine in my bottle will recover him, I will help his ague. Come.

[CALIBAN *drinks*]

Amen. I will pour some in thy other mouth.

TRINCULO Stephano

STEPHANO Doth thy other mouth call me? Mercy, mercy! This is a devil, and no monster. I will leave him; I have no long spoon. 90

TRINCULO Stephano! If thou beest Stephano, touch me, and speak to me; for I am Trinculo – be not afeared – thy good friend Trinculo.

STEPHANO If thou beest Trinculo, come forth! I'll pull thee by the lesser legs. If any be Trinculo's legs, these are they.

[*Pulls him out*]

Thou art very Trinculo indeed! How cam'st thou to be the siege of this moon-calf? Can he vent Trinculos?

TRINCULO I took him to be killed with a thunder-stroke. But art thou not drowned, Stephano? I hope now thou art not drowned. Is the storm over-blown? I hid me under the dead moon-calf's gaberdine for fear of the storm. And art thou living, Stephano? O Stephano, two 100 Neapolitans 'scaped!

[*Embraces* STEPHANO]

Glossary Flats: swamp.
Inch-meal: inch by inch.
Mow: make faces.
Perchance: perhaps.
Mind: notice.
Poor-John: salted, dried fish.
Doit: coin.
Ague: fever.
Siege: excrement.
Moon-calf: monster.

In this scene Stephano, Trinculo and Caliban are drunk. Stephano imagines being ruler of the island and promises to make Caliban his deputy. Trinculo mocks them and Stephano threatens to hang him for mutiny. Caliban begs Stephano to kill Prospero. Ariel makes trouble for Trinculo.

Act III Scene 2 lines 1–79
Near Caliban's cave

Enter CALIBAN, STEPHANO *and* TRINCULO

STEPHANO Tell not me. When the butt is out we will drink water, not a drop before; therefore bear up, and board 'em. Servant monster, drink to me.

TRINCULO [*Aside*] Servant monster? The folly of this island! They say there's but five upon   5 this isle; we are three of them – if th'other two be brained like us, the state totters.

STEPHANO Drink, servant monster, when I bid thee; thy eyes are almost set in thy head.

TRINCULO Where should they be set else? He were a brave monster indeed if they were set in his tail.   10

STEPHANO My man-monster hath drowned his tongue in sack. For my part, the sea cannot drown me – I swam, ere I could recover the shore, five and thirty leagues off and on. By this light, thou shalt be my lieutenant, monster, or my standard.

TRINCULO Your lieutenant if you list; he's no standard.   15

STEPHANO We'll not run, monsieur monster.

TRINCULO Nor go neither; but you'll lie like dogs, and yet say nothing neither.

STEPHANO Moon-calf, speak once in thy life, if thou beest a good moon-calf.   20

CALIBAN How does thy honour? Let me lick thy shoe. I'll not serve him, he is not valiant.

TRINCULO Thou liest, most ignorant monster; I am in case to jostle a constable. Why, thou deboshed fish thou, was there ever man a coward that hath drunk so much sack as I   25 today? Wilt thou tell a monstrous lie, being but half a fish, and half a monster?

CALIBAN Lo, how he mocks me. Wilt thou let him, my lord?

TRINCULO 'Lord', quoth he? That a monster should be such a natural!   30

CALIBAN Lo, lo again! Bite him to death, I prithee.

STEPHANO Trinculo, keep a good tongue in your head. If you prove a mutineer, the next tree. The poor monster's my subject, and he shall not suffer indignity.

CALIBAN I thank my noble lord. Wilt thou be   35 pleased to hearken once again to the suit I made to thee?

STEPHANO Marry will I. Kneel, and repeat it. I will stand, and so shall Trinculo.

Enter ARIEL *invisible*

CALIBAN As I told thee before, I am subject to a tyrant, a sorcerer, that by his cunning hath   40 cheated me of the island.

ARIEL Thou liest.

CALIBAN [*To* TRINCULO] Thou liest, thou jesting monkey thou. I would my valiant master would destroy thee. I do not lie.

STEPHANO Trinculo, if you trouble him any more in's tale, by this hand, I will supplant some of your teeth.   45

TRINCULO Why, I said nothing.

STEPHANO Mum then, and no more. [*To* CALIBAN] Proceed.

CALIBAN I say by sorcery he got this isle; From me he got it. If thy greatness will Revenge it on him – for I know thou dar'st,   50 But this thing dare not –

STEPHANO That's most certain.

CALIBAN Thou shalt be lord of it, and I'll serve thee.

STEPHANO How now shall this be compassed? Canst thou bring me to the party?   55

CALIBAN Yea, yea, my lord, I'll yield him thee asleep,

Where thou mayst knock a nail into his head.

ARIEL Thou liest, thou canst not.

CALIBAN What a pied ninny's this? [*To* TRINCULO] Thou scurvy patch! [*To* STEPHANO] I do beseech thy greatness give him blows,   60
And take his bottle from him. When that's gone,
He shall drink nought but brine, for I'll not show him
Where the quick freshes are.

STEPHANO Trinculo, run into no further danger. Interrupt the monster one word further,   65
and by this hand, I'll turn my mercy out o'doors, and make a stockfish of thee.

TRINCULO Why, what did I? I did nothing. I'll go farther off.

STEPHANO Didst thou not say he lied?

ARIEL Thou liest.

STEPHANO Do I so?   70

[*Strikes* TRINCULO]

Take thou that! As you like this, give me the lie another time.

TRINCULO I did not give the lie. Out o'your wits, and hearing too? A pox o'your bottle! This can sack and drinking do. A murrain on your monster, and the devil take your fingers!

CALIBAN Ha, ha, ha!   75

STEPHANO Now forward with your tale. [*To* TRINCULO] Prithee stand further off.

CALIBAN Beat him enough; after a little time I'll beat him too.

Glossary

Bear up, and board 'em: drink up (a sailors' toast).
Brained like: as clever as.
Set: fixed or staring.
Standard: standard bearer (pun: able to stand).
List: please (pun: lean over like a sinking ship).
Deboshed: drunken.
Natural: idiot.
Suit: request.
Marry: by Saint Mary.
Supplant: uproot.
Compassed: brought about.
Stockfish: dried cod made soft by beating.
Pox: curse.
Murrain: plague.

The Tempest: questions

All of the questions that follow relate to Act II Scene 2

A

Choose just one answer, a, b, c or d.

1 Which is the correct description of the verse used in this scene? **(1 mark)**

a) begins in blank verse and continues in prose ☐

b) begins in prose and continues in blank verse ☐

c) the whole scene is in rhyming couplets ☐

d) the whole scene is in blank verse ☐

2 Which of the following torments is *not* suffered by Caliban? **(1 mark)**

a) led out of his way in the dark ☐

b) hissed at by adders ☐

c) burnt with fire ☐

d) soles of his feet pricked ☐

3 Where does Trinculo find shelter from the weather? **(1 mark)**

a) under his cloak ☐

b) under Caliban's cloak ☐

c) in Prospero's cell ☐

d) under a bush ☐

4 What does Stephano give to Caliban? **(1 mark)**

a) water ☐

b) food ☐

c) a cloak ☐

d) wine ☐

5 Which of the following statements is true? **(1 mark)**

a) Caliban thinks Stephano is one of Prospero's spirits ☐

b) Trinculo thinks Stephano has drowned ☐

c) Stephano thinks Caliban is dead ☐

d) a and b ☐

Score   / 5

B

Answer all parts of all questions.

1 Re-read Caliban's first speech, beginning 'All the infections'.

How does he give the impression of being harshly treated by Prospero?

Support your answer with words and phrases from the text. **(2 marks)**

....

....

2 What does Stephano hope to do with Caliban? **(1 mark)**

....

3 From what they say about Caliban, how do Stephano and Trinculo show that they think he is a monster?
Support your answer with words and phrases from the text. **(4 marks)**

....

....

....

....

Score   / 7

Your answer should respond to each of the bullet points.

1 **In this extract how does Shakespeare create confusion and comedy?**

You should write about:

• what Caliban says and does

• what Stephano and Trinculo say and do

• how each character is confused about the identities of the others. (10 marks)

....

....

....

....

....

....

....

....

....

....

....

....

....

....

....

....

....

....

....

....

....

Score   / 10

Total score   / 22

How well did you do?   ✗   0–6 **Try again**   7–10 **Getting there**   11–14 **Good work**   15–22 **Excellent!** ✓

The Tempest: questions

All of the questions that follow relate to Act III Scene 2

A

Choose just one answer, a, b, c or d.

1 When Stephano threatens Trinculo with 'the next tree', what does he mean? **(1 mark)**

a) he will leave him under it ☐

b) he will hang him from it ☐

c) he will hit him with a branch from it ☐

d) he will have to climb it ☐

2 'If you list' means if you please and if you are falling down. What is the name of this device? **(1 mark)**

a) simile ☐

b) metaphor ☐

c) pun ☐

d) alliteration ☐

3 When Ariel is talking who do the others think it is? **(1 mark)**

a) they know it's Ariel ☐

b) Caliban ☐

c) a ghost ☐

d) Trinculo ☐

4 How does Caliban claim that Prospero gained the island? **(1 mark)**

a) by fighting ☐

b) by magic ☐

c) through marriage ☐

d) by killing the previous ruler ☐

5 What does Caliban say Trinculo will have to drink? **(1 mark)**

a) salt water ☐

b) fresh water ☐

c) wine ☐

d) nothing ☐

Score   / 5

B

Answer all parts of all questions.

1 Re-read Trinculo's first speech, beginning 'Servant Monster?' What does he say about the state of the island and what does this show about his opinion of his companions? **(2 marks)**

....

....

2 Find two examples to show that Stephano considers himself to be Caliban's master and two examples that show Caliban is happy to serve him. **(2 marks)**

Examples: ....

Examples: ....

3 What three things does Stephano threaten Trinculo with? **(3 marks)**

a)..

b)..

c)..

Score   / 7

C   Your answer should respond to each of the bullet points.

1 **In this extract how does Shakespeare present the conflict between Stephano, Trinculo and Caliban?**

You should write about:

• what Trinculo says and does

• how Stephano treats Caliban and Trinculo

• what Ariel adds to the conflict.   (10 marks)

....
....
....
....
....
....
....
....
....
....
....
....
....
....
....
....
....
....
....
....
....
....
....
....

Score   / 10

Total score   / 22

How well did you do?   ✗   0–6 **Try again**   7–10 **Getting there**   11–14 **Good work**   15–22 **Excellent!** ✓

For more help on this topic see KS3 English Success Guide pages 66–75.

75

Spelling

A

Choose just one answer, a, b, c or d.

1 A word which sounds the same as another word but is spelt differently and has a different meaning is a *(1 mark)*

a) homograph ☐

b) homonym ☐

c) homophone ☐

d) synonym ☐

2 Words ending in *ch* are pluralised by adding *(1 mark)*

a) s ☐   b) 's ☐   c) ies ☐   d) es ☐

3 The correct spelling meaning *belonging to it* is *(1 mark)*

a) it's ☐   b) its ☐   c) its' ☐   d) it is ☐

4 *ies* is the correct plural ending of *(1 mark)*

a) all words ending in *y* ☐

b) words ending in a *vowel* then *y* ☐

c) words ending in a *consonant* then *y* ☐

d) words ending in *f* ☐

5 A group of letters added to the beginning of a word to change the meaning is *(1 mark)*

a) a suffix ☐

b) a prefix ☐

c) a synonym ☐

d) an antonym ☐

Score   / 5

B

Answer all parts of all questions.

1 The following words are all spelt incorrectly. Write the correct spelling next to each one. *(10 marks)*

acommodation ....

comited..

strawberrys ....

seperate ....

definate...

churche's (plural)...

leafs ....

possable ....

sucessfull...

beautyful ....

2 Pluralise the following words. *(2 marks)*

monkey   boy   factory   baby   try

....

....

....

3 Write the rule for pluralising words ending in *y*. *(1 mark)*

....

Score   / 13

C

Answer all parts of all questions.

1 There are seven spelling mistakes in the passage below. Find each mistake and write
the correct spellings beneath.

(7 marks)

When he steped back on to the platform, the woman had dissapeared. He scanned the platform
quickley but there was no sign of her. Feeling the weight of the world on his shoulders, he turned
towards the exit and set off for home. As he passed the magazine stand, he cought a flicker of
movement behind the shelfs. It was her, it had to be! He crept behind the stand. How weird – no one
to be scene. Just as he was beginning to think he was imaging things, he saw her again. This time he
wasn't going to let her get away...

a) ....

b) ....

c) ....

d) ....

e) ....

f) ....

g) ....

2 Choose the correct homophone for each sentence that follows.

(7 marks)

The books are on the table over their/they're/there.

Read threw/through your answers before you finish the exam.

Were/We're going on holiday next week.

I cut myself with the sore/saw and now my arm is really sore/saw.

I don't no/know what the answer is.

Did you hear/here that noise?

The not/knot is too tight.

Score   / 14

Total score   / 32

How well did you do?   ✗   0–10 Try again   11–18 Getting there   19–24 Good work   25–32 Excellent! ✓

For more help on this topic see KS3 English Success Guide pages 78–87.

Punctuation and grammar

A

Choose just one answer, a, b, c or d.

1 A simple sentence does *not* contain a (1 mark)

a) main clause ☐

b) comma ☐

c) verb ☐

d) subordinate clause ☐

2 A sentence joining two main clauses with *and* is a (1 mark)

a) simple sentence ☐

b) compound sentence ☐

c) complex sentence ☐

d) concrete sentence ☐

3 Which of the following cannot be used to end a sentence? (1 mark)

a) full stop ☐

b) question mark ☐

c) comma ☐

d) exclamation mark ☐

4 Which of the following statements is incorrect? (1 mark)

a) a sentence usually contains a verb ☐

b) a sentence must begin with a capital letter ☐

c) never begin a sentence with the word *because* ☐

d) sentences don't always end with a full stop ☐

5 An embedded clause (1 mark)

a) splits a main clause ☐

b) ends a sentence ☐

c) is always a main clause ☐

d) must contain a non-finite verb ☐

Score / 5

B

Answer all parts of all questions.

1 Change these two sentences into one compound sentence. (1 mark)

I went to the shop. I bought a chocolate bar.

....

2 Move the subordinate clause in the following sentence, changing the punctuation if necessary. (2 marks)

The trains were late due to track repairs.

....

3 Embed the subordinate clause in the following sentence, changing the punctuation if necessary. (2 marks)

Filled with despair, the teacher marked the exam papers.

....

4 Add apostrophes to the following. (8 marks)

dont	whos (who is)	the poets (singular) writing	doesnt
Joannes bag	the girls (plural) bags	the girls (singular) bag	couldnt

Score / 13

C

Answer all parts of all questions.

1 a) **Give three reasons for beginning a new paragraph.** (3 marks)

i) ....

ii) ....

iii) ....

b) **This extract was originally written in four paragraphs. Identify where paragraphs 2, 3 and 4 should begin.** (3 marks)

John tried to escape through the gate. It was locked, so he tried the other end again. He thought he might be able to climb the fence but every time he tried, he lost his footing. He tried yelling for help even though he knew no one could hear him. When John stopped yelling the silence was deafening. He knew for certain he was trapped and would have to wait until morning. He slid down the fence, head in his hands wondering what had possessed him to come here. Moments later he heard a voice in the darkness. He couldn't believe his ears. "Are you OK sonny?"

Paragraph 1: John tried to escape...

Paragraph 2: ....

Paragraph 3: ....

Paragraph 4: ....

2 **Add the correct punctuation to the following sentences, inserting capital letters.** (8 marks)

a) when the rope snapped the climber who was very frightened fell and broke his leg

....

b) can I go out tonight mum asked Alison

....

c) when the alarm rang the workers left the building calmly

....

d) gosh exclaimed the woman I didn't see you there

....

Score   / 14

Total score   / 32

How well did you do?   ✗ 0–10 **Try again**   11–18 **Getting there**   19–24 **Good work**   25–32 **Excellent!** ✓

For more help on this topic see KS3 English Success Guide pages 78–79 and 88–93.

Paper 1: Reading

- The paper is one hour long plus 15 minutes' reading time.
- Read the three texts provided and answer all the questions that follow.
- Answer each question in the space provided.
- The number of marks available for each task is printed next to the question.

Text 1 – Fiction

Read the three texts that follow and answer all of the questions in the reading section.

In this extract Billy Casper continues his routine to tame and train the kestrel he found when he went nesting.

Billy approached the hawk slowly, regarding it obliquely, clucking and chanting softly, 'Kes Kes Kes'. The hawk bobbed her head and shifted along the perch. Billy held out his gauntlet and offered her a scrap of beef. She reached forward and grasped it with her beak, and tried to pull it from his glove. Billy gripped the beef tightly between forefinger and thumb; and in order to obtain more leverage, the hawk stepped on to his fist. He allowed her to take the beef, then replaced her on the perch, touching the backs of her legs against the wood so that she stepped backwards on to it. He dipped into the leather satchel at his hip and offered her a fresh scrap; this time holding it just out of range of her reaching beak. She bobbed her head and tippled forward slightly, regained balance, then glanced about, uncertain, like someone up on the top board for the first time.

'Come on, Kes. Come on then.'

He stood still. The hawk looked at the meat, then jumped on to the glove and took it. Billy smiled and replaced it with a tough strip of beef, and as the hawk busied herself with it, he attached a swivel to the ends of the jesses dangling from her legs, slipped the jesses between the first and second fingers of his glove, and felt into his bag for the leash. The hawk looked up from her feeding. Billy rubbed his finger and thumb to make the meat move between them, and as the hawk attended to it again, he threaded the leash through the lower ring of the swivel and pulled it all the way through until the knot at the other end snagged on the ring. He completed the security by looping the leash twice round his glove and tying the end round his little finger.

He walked to the door and slowly pushed it open. The hawk looked up, and as he moved out into the full light, her eyes seemed to expand, her body contract as she flattened her feathers. She bobbed her head, once, twice, then bated, throwing herself sideways off his glove and hanging upside down, thrashing her wings and screaming. Billy waited for her to stop, then placed his hand gently under her breast and lifted her back on to the glove. She bated again; and again, and each time Billy lifted her carefully back up, until finally she stayed up, beak half open, panting, glaring round.

'What's up then? What's a matter with you, Kes? Anybody'd think you'd never been out before.'

The hawk roused her feathers and bent to her meat, her misdemeanours apparently forgotten.

Billy walked her round the garden, speaking quietly to her all the time. Then he turned up the path at the side of the house and approached the front gate, watching the hawk for her actions. A car approached. The hawk tensed, watched it then resumed her meal as it sped away up the avenue. On the opposite pavement a little boy, pedalling a tricycle round in tight circles, looked up and saw them, immediately unwound and drove straight off the pavement, making the tin mudguards clank as the wheels jonked down into the gutter. Billy held the hawk away from him, anticipating a bate, but she glanced up at the sound, or at the boy as he cycled towards them and hutched his tricycle up on the pavement.

'Oo that's a smasher. What is it?'

'What tha think it is?'

'Is it an owl?'

'It's a kestrel.'

'Where you got it from?'

'Found it.'

'Is it tame?'

'It's trained. I've trained it.'

Billy pointed to himself, and smiled across at the hawk.

'Don't it look fierce?'

'It is.'

'Does it kill things and eat 'em?'

'Course it does. It kills little kids on bikes.'

The boy laughed without smiling.

'It don't.'

'What's tha think that it's eating now then?'

'It's only a piece of meat.'

'It's a piece o' leg off a kid it caught yesterday. When it catches 'em it sits on their handlebars and rips 'em to pieces. Eyes first.'

The boy looked down at the chrome handlebars and began to swing them from side to side, making the front wheel describe a steady arc like a windscreen wiper.

'I bet I dare stroke it.'

'Tha'd better not.'

'I'll bet I dare.'

'It'll have thi hand off if tha tries.'

The boy stood up, straddling the tricycle frame, and slowly lifted one hand towards the hawk. She mantled her wings over the meat, then struck out with her scaly yellow legs, screaming and raking at the hand with her talons. The boy jerked his arm back with such force that its momentum carried his whole body over the tricycle and on to the ground. He scrambled up, as wide-eyed as the hawk, mounted and pedalled off down the pavement, his legs whirring like bee's wings.

from *A Kestrel for a Knave*
by Barry Hines

Text 2 – Non-fiction

In this extract Douglas Adams describes his experience of scuba diving in Australia, looking for giant manta rays.

For the afternoon dive, Ian said he wanted to take me in a different direction from the boat. I asked him why, and he looked non-committal. I followed him down into the water and slowly we flippered our way across to a new part of the reef. When we reached it, the flat top of the reef was about four feet below the surface, and the sunlight dappled gently over the extraordinary shapes and colours of the brain coral, the antler coral, the sea ferns and anemones. The stuff you see beneath the water often seems like a wild parody of the stuff you see above it. I remember the thought I had when first I dived on the Barrier Reef years ago, which was that this was all the stuff that people used to have on their mantelpieces in the fifties. It took me a while to rid myself of the notion that the reef was a load of kitsch.

I've never learnt the names of a lot of fish. I always swot them up on the boat and forget them a week later. But watching the breathtaking variety of shape and movement keeps me entranced for hours, or would if the oxygen allowed. If I were not an atheist, I think I would have to be a Catholic because if it wasn't the forces of natural selection that designed fish, it must have been an Italian.

I was moving forward slowly in the shallows. A few feet in front of me the reef gradually dipped down into a broad valley. The valley floor was wide and dark and flat. Ian was directing my attention toward it. I didn't know why. There seemed to be just an absence of interesting coral. And then, as I looked, the whole black floor of the valley slowly lifted upward and started gently to waft its way away from us. As it moved, its edges were rippling softly and I could see that underneath it was pure white. I was transfixed by the realisation that what I was looking at was an eight-foot-wide giant manta ray.

It banked away in a wide, sweeping turn in the deeper water. It seemed to be moving breathtakingly slowly, and I was desperate to keep up with it. I came down the side of the reef to follow it. Ian motioned me not to alarm the creature, but just move slowly. I had quickly realised that its size was deceptive and it was moving much more swiftly than I realised. It banked again round the contour of the reef, and I began to see its shape more clearly. It was very roughly diamond-shaped. Its tail is not long, like a sting ray's. The most extraordinary thing is its head. Where you would expect its head to be, it's almost as if something has taken a bite out of it instead. From the two forward points – the outer edges of the 'bite', if you see what I mean – depend two horns, folded downward. And on each of these horns is a single large black eye.

As it moved, shimmering and undulating its giant wings, folding itself through the water, I felt that I was looking at the single most beautiful and unearthly thing I had ever seen in my life. Some people have described them as looking like living stealth bombers, but it is an evil image to apply to a creature so majestic, fluid, and benign.

I followed it as it swam around the outside of the reef. I couldn't follow fast or well, but it was making such wide, sweeping turns that I only had to move relatively short distances round the reef to keep it in sight. Twice, even three times it circled round the reef and then at last it disappeared and I thought I had lost it for good. I stopped and looked around. No. It had definitely gone. I was saddened, but exhilarated with wonder at what I had seen. Then I became aware of a shadow moving on the sea floor at the periphery of my vision. I looked up, unprepared for what I then saw.

The manta ray soared over the top of the reef above me, only this time it had two more in its wake behind it. Together the three vast creatures, moving in perfect, undulating harmony of line, as if following invisible rollercoaster rails, sped off and away till they were lost at last in the darkening distance of the water.

I was very quiet that evening as we packed the Sub Bug back into its big silver box. I thanked Ian for finding the manta rays. I said I understood about not riding them.

'Ah, no worries, mate,' he said. 'No worries at all.'

from *The Salmon of Doubt*
by Douglas Adams

Text 3 – Media text

APO

giving animals the protection they deserve.

Animal **P**rotection **O**rganisation

Home   About APO   Animal Stories   Rehabilitation   Get Involved   Make a Donation

Animal Stories

Mog's Tale

Alfie's Story

A Dog's Life

Rehabilitation

How you can help

Find your nearest APO centre

◄ up to 10 miles

◄ your postcode

search

Results...

Sign up for our email information service

Register

Donate online now

Mog's Tale

Just months ago, this beautiful little kitten was unrecognisable after being subjected to terrifying cruelty.

She had been wrapped in sellotape and the tip of her tail had been badly damaged – probably repeatedly stamped on.

She was brought to one of our rescue centres where trained volunteers work alongside vets to care for animals injured or neglected by careless owners.

Thanks to their round the clock care and attention, Mog has made a good recovery. Her fur has re-grown and although the tip of her tail has been amputated she is able to jump and balance without any problems.

Mog has now been found a safe and loving home. She is learning to enjoy life as a proper family pet.

Not so lucky

Believe it or not, Mog is one of the lucky ones! Every year hundreds of animals are brought to our centres around the country and even our expert care cannot save them. That's why we need your help and generous donations to continue our fight to prevent this mindless cruelty happening in the first place.

We need your help!

Whether it is your time volunteering, your generous donations of money or your support for our campaign work, we cannot continue to be successful without you. Kittens like Mog need your help and just a small regular gift of £2 a month could make all the difference in a life or death situation.

Click here to make a donation now.

Reading test

You have one hour to complete this test. Answer all of the questions.

The spaces for each answer and the number of marks indicate how much you need to write.

Questions 1–6 are about *A Kestrel for a Knave*.

1 **Complete the following table, giving one thing that Billy does with each item.**   (1 mark)

Item	What Billy does
scrap of beef	
swivel	
leash	

2 **What does the hawk do when it bates? Tick one box.**   (1 mark)

Fly away   ☐

Hang upside down from the glove   ☐

Eat a scrap of meat   ☐

Freeze and remain silent   ☐

3 **Look at the section 'Billy approached the hawk slowly' to 'tying the end round his little finger'.**   (4 marks)

From this section how do you know that Billy knows a lot about how to deal with the hawk?

Give two examples of what he says or does and explain how this shows he is very knowledgeable.

Example: ....

Explanation: ....

....

....

Example: ....

Explanation: ....

....

....

4 **Look at the conversation between Billy and the boy on the tricycle.**
Why does the boy 'laugh without smiling'? (2 marks)

....

....

....

....

....

5 **Look at the final paragraph, beginning 'The boy stood up, straddling the tricycle frame'.**
How does the writer create a sense of the boy's fear in this paragraph?
You should write about:

• the way the hawk is described

• the language used to describe the boy's actions. (5 marks)

....

....

....

....

....

....

....

....

....

....

....

6 **How does the writer create the sense that Billy is at ease with the wild bird he is training?**

You should write about:

- the way Billy behaves towards the hawk
- the way the hawk responds to Billy
- the difference between the hawk's behaviour with Billy and with the boy on the tricycle. (6 marks)

....

....

....

....

....

....

....

....

....

....

....

....

....

....

....

....

....

....

....

....

....

....

Questions 7–12 are about *The Salmon of Doubt*

7 **Look at the paragraph beginning 'I was moving forward slowly'.**

How does the writer create a feeling of slow, gentle movement?
Give one example and explain what effect it has.

(2 marks)

Example:...

....

Explanation:...

....

8 **What does the phrase 'I was transfixed by the realisation' suggest about how the writer felt about seeing a manta ray?**

(2 marks)

....

....

....

....

....

9 **Look at the paragraph beginning 'As it moved'. Give two examples from the paragraph that show how the writer feels about the manta ray and explain why each is effective.**

(2 marks)

Example:...

....

Explanation:...

....

....

....

Example:...

....

Explanation:...

....

....

....

10 Look at the section 'No. It had definitely gone' to 'distance of the water'.

Why does the writer feel 'saddened but exhilarated'? **(2 marks)**

....

....

....

11 How does the writer create a feeling of excitement and surprise in this section? **(4 marks)**

....

....

....

....

....

....

....

....

12 How successful is the writer in recreating his underwater experience?

You should write about:

• how he sets the scene

• his description of the manta ray

• the way he involves the reader. **(5 marks)**

....

....

....

....

....

....

....

....

Questions 13–16 are about the APO webpage

13 **What is the purpose of this webpage? Give two methods used to achieve this purpose.** (3 marks)

Purpose:...

....

....

a) ....

....

b) ....

....

14 **Find and copy an example of a fact and an opinion used in the text.** (1 mark)

Fact:...

....

....

Opinion:...

....

....

15 **In the sections 'Not so lucky' and 'We need your help!' which personal pronouns are most often used and what effect does this have?** (2 marks)

Personal pronouns:..

....

....

....

Explanation: ....

....

....

....

16 **Comment on the overall effectiveness of the use of language, layout and presentation devices to persuade the reader to donate via the APO website.**

You should write about:

- specific words and phrases
- use of pictures
- font size and style
- general organisation. (5 marks)

....
....
....
....
....
....
....
....
....
....
....
....
....
....
....
....
....
....
....
....
....
....

Paper 2: Writing

Section A

You have 45 minutes to complete this test.

You should spend 15 minutes planning your answer.

Complete your plan in the space below. Write your answer on a separate sheet of paper.

This task is worth 30 marks. You will be awarded marks for:

- **sentence structure and punctuation** (8 marks)
- **text structure and organisation** (8 marks)
- **composition and effect.** (14 marks)

Imagine that you do some volunteer work for a local animal sanctuary which takes in stray and neglected pets as well as caring for injured wild animals and birds. The animal sanctuary will have to close in three months' time unless extra funding can be raised.

Write a letter to your local council to persuade them to give a grant to the animal sanctuary.

Make your writing as persuasive as possible but remember it is a formal letter.

Planning sheet

Make brief notes under the following headings:

Services provided by the animal sanctuary

....

....

What the money is needed for

....

....

Benefits to the council and local community

....

....

Word bank

List any persuasive/emotive words or phrases you might use in your letter.

....

....

Section B

You have 30 minutes to complete this test.

You should spend 5–10 minutes planning your writing.

Complete your plan in the space below. Write your answer on a separate sheet of paper.

This task is worth 20 marks. You will be awarded marks for:

• sentence structure/punctuation and text organisation   (6 marks)

• composition and effect   (10 marks)

• spelling.   (4 marks)

You have been asked to write a contribution for the school magazine about your ambitions and plans for the future.

Write a short article in which you explain what your ambition is, how you hope to achieve it and how you would feel if you were able to do this.

Planning sheet

Make brief notes under the following headings:

Ambition

....

....

....

....

How to achieve ambition

....

....

....

....

Feelings

....

....

....

....

Paper 3: Shakespeare (reading & understanding)

The printed extracts relating to these questions are:

Romeo and Juliet	**Pages 52–55**
As You Like It	**Pages 60–63**
The Tempest	**Pages 68–71**

Answer the question about the Shakespeare play you have studied or the general question that best fits the play and scenes you have studied.

1 *Romeo and Juliet*: Act III Scene 2 and Act III Scene 5

In these scenes Juliet's love for Romeo is put to the test as she finds out what has happened to Tybalt and must decide whether to obey her father or face the consequences of staying true to Romeo.

How does Shakespeare show the strength of Juliet's feelings for Romeo in these scenes?

....

....

....

....

2 *As You Like It*: Act I Scene 1 and Act II Scene 3

In these scenes Shakespeare introduces a brotherly relationship full of hatred between Oliver and Orlando and a master / servant relationship full of loyalty and high regard between Orlando and Adam.

How would you direct these scenes to reveal the differences between Orlando's relationship with Oliver and his relationship with Adam?

....

....

....

....

3 *The Tempest*: Act II Scene 2 and Act III Scene 2

In the play Caliban exchanges one cruel master, Prospero, for a drunken one, Stephano. He seems happy to be treated badly by Stephano.

How does Shakespeare present the relationship between Stephano, Trinculo and Caliban in these scenes?

....

....

....

....

General questions

Answer the question that best fits the play and specific scenes you have studied. Write your answers on a separate sheet.

Text in performance

How would you direct two key scenes from the Shakespeare play you have studied to create an appropriate atmosphere?

You should:

- give direction about how characters should behave
- give direction about how lines should be spoken
- give explanation about why a particular atmosphere is required.

Character and motivation

Comment on the behaviour of the main character(s) in two key scenes from the Shakespeare play you have studied.

You should write about:

- the language they use
- the way they behave towards other characters
- how their character(s) change or develop between the two scenes.

Character and motivation

How does Shakespeare use language to demonstrate the inner feelings of a character in two key scenes you have studied?

You should write about:

- use of imagery
- the difference between what the character says when alone on stage and what s/he says to others.

Ideas, themes and issues

How does Shakespeare use these scenes to explore an issue that would have concerned his audience?

You should write about:

- how this issue is introduced
- how character behaviour might reflect or challenge the audience's opinion about the issue
- how language is used to explore the issue.

Notes